SLATE QUARRYING
AT CORRIS

Slate Quarrying
at Corris

Alun John Richards

GWASG Carreg
Gwalch

ISBN: 0-86381-279-1

Cover photo:
Aerial view of Foel Grochan

First published in 1994 by Gwasg Carreg Gwalch,
Iard yr Orsaf, Llanrwst, Gwynedd,
Wales
℡ 01492 642031
Printed and published in Wales.

Map of Corris Quarries:
Ken Lloyd Gruffydd

CONTENTS

MAPS

PHOTOGRAPHS

ACKNOWLEDGEMENTS

I am indebted to:

Mr Jeremy Wilkinson for so much research guidance generously given.

Mr J.F. Lloyd, Managing Director of Wincilate Ltd, for making his records available.

The officers of the Corris Railway Society, for access to their documents.

The many ex-quarrymen and other people of Corris and district, for giving me their time and their memories.

The staffs of the Gwynedd Archives Service and the National Library of Wales for their patience.

The Friends of Tan y Bwlch for their sponsorship.

Most of all, my wife Delphine for her constant encouragement and assistance both in the field and in the archives.

A.J.R.

WARNING

All quarries are on private ground and permission must be obtained to visit them, not only to go onto the land occupied by the quarries but also any other land that must be crossed to reach them.

All slate quarries are dangerous, slippery underfoot, with unstable tips, possibly unguarded shafts, and faces, and the likelihood of rockfalls.

Underground. ALL in the area are **DANGEROUS** and should not be entered. Where details of underground geography are given, it is for record purposes only, **NOT** as a guide to would-be trespassers.

RHAGAIR

Mae Corris yn ardal a gafodd, yn fwy na heb, ei hanwybyddu'n llwyr gan yr hanesydd diwydiannol. Ceir amryw lyfrau ar Reilffordd Corris, a rhai cyhoeddiadau cyffredinol sy'n crybwyll y chwareli. Llyfr Alun John yw'r adroddiad cyhoeddedig cyntaf ar raddfa lawn i gofnodi chwarelyddiaeth Llechi yng Nghorris.

Ceisiodd yr awdur osgoi ailadrodd blinderus o fanylion am ffurfio cwmni a.y.y.b. gan geisio cyflwyno i'r darllenydd hanes taith y diwydiant yn y gymuned ddiddorol hon, weithiau i fyny, weithiau i lawr, gyda phwyslais ar rai o'r cymeriadau a gymerodd ran ynddi. Mae'n tynnu sylw at le blaengar Corris yng nghynhyrchiad Llech o'r radd flaenaf ac yn nodi fod hyn yn parhau. Ychydig iawn o gynnwys y lyfr sydd wedi ei gyhoeddi eisoes. Roedd y gwaith ymchwil yn cynnwys edrych ar rai dogfennau nad ŷnt ar gael i'r cyhoedd. Ychwanegwyd at yr ymchwil trwy gyfweliadau, gwaith maes, ac o wybodaeth fanwl a'r awdur ei hunan o'r ardal.

Mae'n bleser gan Gyfeillion Tan y Bwlch noddi cyhoeddiad hwn sy'n dilyn llyfr cyntaf Alun John "A Gazeteer of the Welsh Slate Industry" a brofodd i fod mor llwyddiannus. Dymuwn y gorau i Alun John gyda'r "Chwarelyddiaeth yng Nghorris."

Mona Williams, Cadeirydd, Cyfeillion Tan y Bwlch

PREFACE

Corris is a region almost totally ignored by the industrial historian. There have been several books on the Corris Railway, and some more general works, none of which deal in detail with the quarries.

Alun John's book is the first full-scale published record of slate quarrying in Corris.

He has avoided repetition of tiresome detail of company formations etc., but rather has made it a readable journey through its ups and downs, with some emphasis on the characters involved in the industry of this fascinating community. He has called attention to Corris's pre-eminence in the production of high quality slab and the fact that it is still continuing.

The book contains very little that has been previously published. The research, which included some documents not in public archives, has been backed by interviews, field work and his own detailed knowledge of the area.

The Friends of Tan y Bwlch are very pleased to have helped sponsor this book and wish Alun John the same success as he had with his "Gazeteer of the Welsh Slate Industry."

Mona Williams, Chairman, Friends of Tan y Bwlch

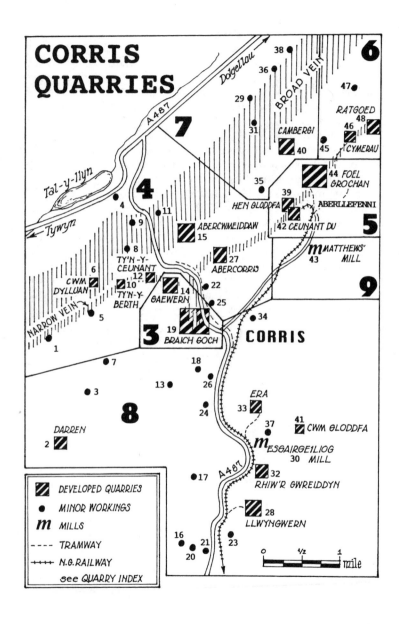

Section 1 SLATE QUARRYING AT CORRIS

Corris, to the traveller, is an almost unnoticed interruption on a journey from Machynlleth to Dolgellau. A couple of short restricted sections of the A487, where, after the winding, tree-lined climb along the river Dulas, the scenery widens prior to the swoop down into the spectacular Talyllyn Valley. Most will spare but a glance for the abandoned heaps of slate waste, vanishing under landscaping or encroaching forestry; the clustered cottages or the serried ranks of slate headstones. If a stop is made it will be a mere pause at the Visitor Centre.

Though well known for its Narrow Gauge railway, the Slate Quarries which that line served and on which the whole area was economically dependant, have gone largely unrecorded. None were really big, few particularly successful, but their innovative methods and the excellence of their products made a significant contribution to the Welsh Slate Quarrying scene.

Their men toiled for small and uncertain reward, at least 20 suffering violent death, many times this number dying of injuries or disease, in this most dangerous of callings. Their wives, or their widows, eked pittances to raise families on a barren rocky terrain. Together they developed a proud and enduring cultural tradition.

The owners though not as rapacious as some in other areas, often lacked acumen and soundness, and rarely made the sort of profits which might have enabled them to be more generous towards their employees. Constantly, both masters and men were in the iron grip of the ebb and flow of prices and market demand in a "boom and bust" industry. Which in Corris' case often meant more bust than boom.

From early times Slate had been prised from outcrops of the valleys of the Afon Dulas and its tributaries, when the need arose for a roof-covering in the locality.

By about the beginning of the 16th century some Aberllefenni slate was making the difficult journey to Aberdyfi or Derwenlas for shipment further afield. This, by about 1810, had become a small but established trade.

However, up to the first decades of the 19th Century when the slate industry was developing apace at Blaenau Ffestiniog and in

11

Caernarfonshire, most of the few inhabitants of the narrow Dulas valleys were still scratching an agrarian subsistence. As contemporary reports have it, "grazing sheep in the declevities of the hills", and raising cattle and crops on the "not altogether unproductive lower grounds".

The existence of the main Veins was known, the "Broad Vein" of greyish slate, the magnificent "Narrow Vein" to the south of it, and the rich Braich Goch "Appendix". But, except where the valley road, such as it was, met the desirable Narrow Vein at Aberllefenni, cartage costs and breakages made quarrying in the area an unattractive venture.

The 1830s abolition of the tax on coastwise slate with the rise of prices and expansion of trade which followed it, spurred investors to seek new sites. By 1835, with the completion of the new Coach road, (the present A487), quarrying on the Dulas became a realistic proposition and serious exploitation commenced at what we now know as Upper Corris.

By 1849 the *Topographical Directory of Wales* was reporting 1500 tons of slate shipped annually at Derwenlas. A fraction of a percent of the Welsh total, but enough to mark Corris as a slate producing area.

Unfortunately, by this time the expansions at Penrhyn, Dinorwig, Nantlle and Blaenau, and contractions elsewhere, had shown that economics demanded a direct railed link to the coast. The Corris carts would not do.

At last, in 1859 the opening of the Corris, Machynlleth & River Dovey Tramroad (later the Corris Railway), provided that vital link. The timing was most opportune for the price of slate was firming up, and over the next 15 years or so, best slates rose by some 86%. Moreover the price of second quality, which, in all honesty, was often more representative of the Corris roofing product, more than doubled. By 1875 almost a dozen quarries were in production and the Corris Railway was carrying approaching 20,000 tons of slate per year, which, Blaenau Ffestiniog apart, was well over half the Meirionnydd total.

The social impact must have been immense. The population increased tenfold, houses were built, (many by quarry owners), chapels founded, shops and businesses established. Cash ceased to be a rare and seasonal item since the quarry wages, meagre though they were, must have represented greater sums circulating monthly, than, in earlier days, the area would have seen in a year.

Regrettably this bonanza was short lived. After the mid 70s prices wavered, dropped dramatically in 1879 and by the mid 1880s were down by a third, the lower qualities being affected more than the best. In fact prices actually realised would have been even less since in times of slump, heavy discounting of List Prices was usual. When returns dropped, quarries had at best to lay men off and, at worst to go bankrupt, so from about 1880 on, employment became increasingly uncertain.

Prices did slowly recover in the early 1890s, advanced strongly in 1896, and by 1903 (due to the shortage caused by the 1900-03 Penrhyn stoppage), roofing slate prices had regained their 1876 levels. Unfortunately, Corris by this time was increasingly dependant on the by now, shrinking slab market, so that even in 1902, at the height of the desperate roofing slate shortage, tonnages failed to regain the mid 1870s figures.

Several factors exacerbated Corris' problems. By the 1860s when railed transport enabled the area to be seriously competitive, the "The Golden Age" of Welsh Slate was more than half over. Corris had to enter a mature and discerning market, selling against big quarries of long established repute. When the going got tough, those bigger, longer established quarries of Caernarfonshire and Blaenau, often had muscle and reserves, as well as export markets to look to, the Corris quarries generally did not.

This apart, Corris costs were higher than the northern areas; the Veins were narrower and the steep valleys constrained development, confined tipping space and restricted water catchment. The difficulties of working are confirmed by the fact that whilst the industry average of 30 tons output per man/year was comfortably exceeded in many quarries elsewhere, in Corris such a figure was considered high. Carriage too, was dearer, the C.R.'s rates being invariably higher than say the Ffestiniog Railway and, in the case of roofing slate, Corris' products tended to be thicker, costing more per thousand to transport.

By 1906 prices were down almost to those of the lean years of the 1880s with the tile makers and the importers tightening their grip on the market. The Braich Goch closure came as a hammer blow, and at the surviving quarries, the cycle of dismissal followed by re-employment, continued, but, increasingly the numbers taken on failed to match those discharged. The near terminal decline had set in.

When the war came, slate was classed as "non-essential", the men went to the forces or the munition factories, and the industry faded to near nothingness.

A dramatic revival came in 1918/9 with quarterly revisions taking prices to more than twice pre-war levels. By 1921 prices of Bests had put on a further 5% with Seconds even more. But, once again the upturn was mainly the roofing product, and Corris quarries now even more Slab dependant, were unable to derive much benefit. The scramble for manpower in booming Caernarfonshire and Blaenau pushed wages almost out of reach of the Corris owners, and the inflated prices of plant discouraged expansion.

The bubble burst in 1922, prices fell, but not costs. Most of the larger quarries of North Wales were able to ride the storms of the 20's and 30's, the smaller quarries could not. Corris became increasingly marginalised.

1939 brought a replay of 1914's events, but this time, post-war, there was the merest boomlet, and the slide resumed, eventually leaving only 2 Corris quarries open, one of these closing in 1966. Elsewhere in Wales several quarries re-opened in the 1980's, but the geology and topography around the Dulas does not lend itself to the sort of vigorous un-topping methods which up-to-date techniques permit, and modern economics demand.

Thus we are left with one, almost anachronistic survival — Aberllefenni — whose excellent rock, energetic management and small but dedicated workforce find a market niche, for a slab product which finds a demand, almost world-wide, for those who insist on the best.

This has left Corris a very changed place the population more than halved. Out of 10-12 chapels, only one survives and Holy Trinity church has a small and ageing congregation, of the more than a score of shops, few still trade. Gone are the choirs, bands and many of the people, some back to the North Wales of their forbears, some to the mines of South Wales, some to make their mark further afield. Gone too, are the 34 men who died in two wars.

Of those who remain, many travel long miles to find work, incomers, many retired, are numerous. Yet it is not the decaying dormitory it might well have become. Less obvious, less vibrant than in the past, the pride and independence of this fine community remains.

THE QUARRIES

This study is confined to the quarries of the valleys of the river Dulas and its tributaries. Some might, with sound geological justification, take a wider area, including, for instance, the Angell valley, where the Hendre Ddu and other quarries worked the same rock, sold slab to the same customers and to some extent exchanged labour. Lines have to be drawn somewhere, and by taking the Dulas valley definition we have a compact group, that was intertwined, economically and socially and shared a common transport route.

THE CORRIS RAILWAY

Every quarry was as utterly dependant on this 2' 3"g. line, as it was on them. Yet like a couple in some domestic drama, shackled by necessity it co-existed with the quarries in smouldering mutual distrust, punctuated by fierce dispute.

Opened in 1859 as the Corris, Machynlleth & River Dovey Tramroad, as a horse drawn line it connected the quarries to a shipping point on the Dyfi at Derwenlas, which had been a long established shipping point for carted product. When the Cambrian Railway opened at Machynlleth in 1867, trans-shipment sidings were laid and the tramway south west of the town became disused, and the name Corris Railway was adopted, In 1879 the line was steamed, and shortly afterwards opened for passenger traffic. The decline of the quarries brought inexorable shrinkage. Passengers having been surrendered to the motor bus in 1931, final closure came in 1948.

The trackbed at the Aberllefenni terminus, with its fine set of slate access steps, is obvious. It first approximately follows the road and then goes through fields to Corris where there is a nice bridge and part of the station buildings now house the Corris Railway

Museum. From Corris to the engine shed at Maespoeth about ½ mile distant, track has been relaid, by the Corris Railway Society. From Maespoeth to about ½ mile short of Machynlleth, it can be almost continuously traced alongside the main road. There are several 'bus shelter' stations still standing. Vestiges of the branches to Ceinws and Llwyngwern can be seen.

After leaving the main road it cuts directly across fields to Machynlleth station, via the remains of the Dyfi bridge, whose collapse precipitated closure. Alongside the present Machynlleth station, some of the terminus buildings of the Corris Railway are in re-use. The bricked up arch where the main road passes under the railway denoted the path of the original tramway, which can be intermittently traced to the shipping point near Derwenlas.

There were 3 feeder tramways. The most important was the Upper Corris tramway which ran down the western bank of the river from Corris Uchaf. Much now forms a foot-path. At Corris it passed close alongside the main road, in a gulley between the road and houses, little accommodation bridges still being in use. It crossed the Aberllefenni road on the level, through what is now the Braich Goch Hotel car park, and alongside the main road to make a junction with the Corris Railway at Maespoeth.

The most interesting branch was the Ratgoed tramway which ran from that quarry to make an end-on junction at Aberllefenni. Apart from serving the quarries, this branch was the sole means of transport in the valley, and when the C.R. closed consideration was given to keeping it open for the same sort of "social reasons" as were to figure in talk of main line closures in later years. Most of the formation remains, partly as a track and partly as a forestry road.

The remaining branch was the short line from the Aberllefenni quarry itself, to the Aberllefenni mill. It ran alongside the road and was in use, (latterly tractor powered) until the 1970's and in fact the trackwork outside the mill was not lifted until 1989.

Section 2 THE SLATE AND THE MEN

THE PRODUCT

The main product of the industry was, and still is, roofing material. Since the late 18th century, it has been made in standard sizes, traditionally known by "Female Nobility" names such as Duchess's, Ladies etc. At various times there were 2,3 & 4 qualities, the best being the thinnest and freest from blemish. These were sold in "Milles" of 1200. Small miscellaneous slates ("Ton" slates and "Moss" slates) were sold by weight.

As Corris slate, particularly, from the Narrow Vein, is dense and often does not split readily, much of the product from the region, especially latterly, was Slab.

Today the use of Slab is mainly confined to plaques and the detail of prestige buildings. However in the 19th century, and before, its permanence, and comparative cheapness caused it to be widely used for flooring, cills and lintels and fireplaces. Corris Slab was strong enough to be used even for coalhole covers. (Cars still drive over them without ill effect).

It was also, of course the standard tombstone material. Its imperviousness made it attractive for cisterns, farm fittings and sanitary use. Its high specific heat made it ideal for cold slabs in dairies and larders. Later, its dielectric properties made it the standard switchboard material for electricity sub-station and distribution systems.

After the 1825 invention of the "Slate bed" billiards table, these took an appreciable tonnage, and later even "Shove-H'penny" boards were made out of slate.

Slab was originally sold by the square foot, but from the mid 19th century, by the ton, in "promiscuous" lengths and breadths, usually priced in 3 categories — 2'6" — 5' long x 3' wide, 5' — 7' long x 2' & upwards wide, & 7' upwards long x 3' upwards wide (or over 24 square feet super).

Each category was available in ¾" — 2" thicknessess (in normally ¼"steps), the two smaller categories also being available in ½". These were usually planed on both sides. A surcharge was made for exact sizes. "Common Flagging", which was unplaned, was also offered.

Most quarries did "Mantel Sets", Cisterns (priced by capacity), Headstones and other specialities. But these were often made by outside traders, to whom the quarries sold the part-finished Slab. An unusually high proportion of Corris slate was Enamelled, either by the quarries or by their customers (Section 9).

Other Slate products included Writing Slates, and tool sharpening Hones, but there was little Corris involvement in either of these.

Sales were normally made through merchants, who might be specialist Slate dealers, manufacturers of Slate products or be general builders suppliers. It was customary both to put "consignment" stock into these traders yards, which was only invoiced when sold and to grant credit of 3 months or so. A quarry stock inventory always included substantial tonnages in these yards, which involved tying up considerable capital and heavy write downs if prices dropped.

These "Middlemen", were often in a big way of business enjoying considerable standing in the trade. They provided an outlet for the product to quarries too small (as Corris units generally were) to have a marketing organisation of their own. They, to an extent, protected the quarry from bad debt, since they tended to be more creditworthy, than the notoriously volatile building trade. Most importantly, since a Slate quarry has to produce sizes and qualities according to the rock being obtained rather than what buyers may be currently requiring, they could take into stock and energetically seek outlets for varieties which might be temporarily in poor demand. They usually worked on a 10-15% discount, and for roofing slate, got 1260 count per Mille.

Prices were on an "ex-quarry" basis, Corris quarries normally arranging delivery to Machynlleth station (or in early days, to the wharf), the Corris Railway freight and handling charges being added to the invoice. Occasionally shipments to say, Ireland, would be organised by the quarry and at one time Aberllefeni had their own vessel.

Direct sales to an end user were rare until recent times, and were likely to be small quantities picked up from the quarry by local builders.

Winning the Slate

The Broad Vein quarries at Corris were generally worked opencast. Typically starting as a hillside working on one or more terraces, then possibly developing into a pit, accessed and drained by a cutting or tunnel.

The Narrow Vein quarries were mostly worked underground. But even on the Broad Vein, initial trials would normally be underground, to enable assessment to be made with minimum excavation. A typical sequence of events when an outcrop was found on a hillside, was for it to be dug into to "Break cover". Then if it showed promise, a tunnel was driven from say 25 yards lower downslope, and from it, "A roof raised" to meet the original excavation.

The classic method of underground quarrying, on anything but the smallest scale, was to cut a "strike" tunnel across Vein and work upwards from it at several points, developing a series of chambers possibly 100 feet wide, leaving pillars of slate of perhaps 50 feet between the chambers to support the ground above. The strike tunnels could be duplicated at perhaps 70 foot vertical intervals so that chambers could be developed on several levels or "floors", extraction in each continuing upward until the floor of the next chamber above was quarried away. In the near vertical Veins at Aberllefenni a most unusual method of downward working was pioneered.

High Explosive might be used for development tunnelling, but all blasting of slate rock was done with Black Powder. The shot holes for this were, latterly, drilled by compressed air drills but traditionally the "Jwmpar" was used. This was weighted iron rod upwards of 6 feet long which by repeatedly throwing it against the rock, produced a hole. Progression was perhaps 6″ — 12″ per exhausting hour. Great skill was required in siting the shot holes to make use of natural faults in the rock, to ensure a maximum yield of usable block. Even so 75-80% and more waste, was commonplace.

Reducing the slate

After blasting, usable blocks which were oversized would be divided, usually by skilled hitting with the large, African-Oak headed mallet (Y Rhys).

In small quarries the rough blocks were then entirely hand-worked. They would first be reduced to approximate rectangles of suitable size. Then split with hammer and broad-bladed chisel into thin sheets, for roofing slate or into greater thicknesses for Slab. Roofing slates were trimmed to exact size and squareness by striking with a cranked knife whilst supported on a straight-edge. Slab was squared by chiselling or by handsawing with a toothless saw and a plentiful supply of wet sand.

By the time quarrying became seriously established at Corris, mechanised sawing was the norm. The first mechanical saws were Sandsaws, virtually just a powering, invariably by water, of the original handsaws. These were supplemented by circular saws, (sometimes, when power was unavailable, handcranked!). Sawing machines were housed in a mill, which usually also had planing machines, for the final surfacing of Slab. Often the mill would only deal with Slab product, roofing slate still being handworked at or near the face, or in the case of underground quarries, near the adit, in open-fronted dressing sheds or "waliau".

A few Corris quarries had "integrated" mills where blocks for roofing slates too, were sawn. Such mills would also have rotary trimming machines for the final trimming to size of the roofing slates. Although, as with Slab, the splitting was a hand operation, as a satisfactory machine for splitting has, even today, yet to be devised.

Besides the actual dexterity called for in splitting slate, considerable judgement is required to assess the correct moisture content, and drying, weathering or moistening with wet sacks may be called for, to achieve a good split. The modern availability of diamond circular saws up to 2m. diameter and, uniquely at Aberllefenni of a reciprocating gang saw, has enabled sawing on the "third axis", thus largely obviating splitting of at least the smaller Slab. Larger Slab still has sometimes to be split, and the splitting of a block perhaps 8' x 4' or more, into slabs up to 2" thick requires not just skill, but heroism. Also still occasionally called for when a block is too big for the saws, is the old art of dividing blocks by the use of the big mallet, or the "plug and feathers".

A few mills had sand and water polishing machines, where superfine finishes were called for. Nowadays diamond polishers are used, but even with these, the best work has to be hand-finished with emery cloth. Special machines were, and still are, used for "fancy" edgings etc.

Handling the slate

All quarries had rail lines (in the Corris area, 2' 3" Gauge), if only to handle the waste, larger quarries having extensive systems. Differences in level generally being dealt with by self-acting inclines, normally on the surface, but sometimes underground. The practice, found in some Corris quarries of lowering material down vertical shafts to cope with changes in level underground, was uncommon elsewhere.

The self-acting inclines were two-tracked, the weight of a downgoing load hauling up empty wagons by means of a rope wound round a (usually) horizontal drum, controlled by a brake. Where upward movement was required, inclines were powered by Water-balance, by Water-wheel, by Steam, or, occasionally, underground by Compressed Air.

Blocks were carried on flat-bedded waggons. Loading might be by sheer-legs, small hand-crane, or in the case of underground working by a winch with a cable reeved through a block fixed to the roof. Unloading in the mill was usually by overhead gantry or tackle.

Waste, the one-off development waste, the recurrent quarrying waste, the mill waste and trimmings would, ideally, be tipped, via open-fronted trucks onto handy downsloping ground, hopefully away from areas of possible future extraction. In the constricted valleys around Corris, this was often difficult. Sometimes an advantage could be created out of an necessity, by using waste to provide a level platform for a mill and stocking area. Some quarries had to truck considerable distances to dump, some had to uphaul, others had to build vast retaining walls to contain the tips. An alternative in underground working was to backfill quarry waste into abandoned chambers, but this risked sterilising chambers that might be wanted for further working at a later date.

THE MEN AND THEIR MASTERS

In the earliest days slate was won by partnerships in tiny

diggings, who perhaps might sell their product to entrepreneurs. When, due to machanisation, slate quarrying required capital and formal quarries were set up, this tradition was in effect carried on by the Bargain system.

A group, generally of 4 men would, usually on a 4 week basis, negotiate a price for winning a particular stretch of rock and reducing it to slates or Slab. This normally meant they would, in effect agree to accept a figure, based on a "Letting Standard" plus an amount which hopefully would reflect the outturn of the rock. The men would endeavour to secure a high rate for poor rock, accepting a lower rate for good, easily worked rock. Thus the team was virtually an independent firm. The system was in many ways unsatisfactory, giving rise to corrupt practices (from which Corris quarries were remarkably free) but it was staunchly clung to by the men, membership of a Bargain being a proud privilege.

A quarryman once told the author of how, as a boy, his father would borrow a warehouse truck from the "Old Shop" at Upper Corris to fetch small blocks from an abandoned quarry, so that he, the boy, could practise splitting and trimming it, thus when the time came for him to start work, he could be assured an early place in a Bargain.

Other workers would include "Badrockmen" paid on tonnage to remove non-productive rock. "Rubblers" cleared the waste, these and other labourers might include young boys waiting for a place in a Bargain gang.

There might also be tradesmen such as carpenters and masons, on a daily rate, but that most important person, the smith was sometimes an independent tradesman who charged the men for sharpening tools and the company for other work. If he was an employee, it was usual for the quarry to make a deduction for smith work. The men also, up to well into the 20th Century, were charged for powder, candles and other consumables.

As regards owners, Corris never attracted the worst type, but it did not always attract the best. Few were downright dishonest, but many spurred by tales of wealth in Caernarfonshire, sought the "fast buck" with dubious promotions. Others pressed, sometimes incompetent managers, into working for short term gains rather than long term prospects. Some invested too little, others too much. Backers originally came mainly from outside the area but later local traders and professional men appeared. Most lost their shirts.

It was chiefly only those owners who were independent men of substance, who prospered and offered sound and reasonably continuous employment.

Section 3 BRAICH GOCH & GAEWERN

These two quarries dominated the Corris scene, socially, economically and visually, for almost a century and a half.

Gaerwern, where the Narrow Vein starts to double back into the "Appendix", developed out of 3 separate diggings, Sgwd, Rhognat and Glanderi. All or some of which may have been worked from an early time. Tap Maior at Cae Coch on Braich Goch on the Appendix proper, may also have been the site of some early, very small scale, extraction. Real development only came when good road access became available.

The Braich Goch Appendix Vein, is an anomaly where the rock was subjected to additional pressures producing a most desirable slate which is denser, and of bluer colour than the Narrow Vein proper. The penalty for this excellence was the extreme thinness of the vein — 20 yards, at the most, increasing the cost of extraction which was never fully reflected in any premium obtainable for the product. They were best known for Slab, but a great deal of excellent roofing slate was produced.

Gaewern, until it came under common ownership, and joint working, with Braich Goch, had a somewhat eventful career, opening as it did at a time of much speculative activity in the industry, and Braich Goch itself was scarcely a model of commercial propriety in pre-Birley days. They had their ups and downs, reflecting the "feast or famine" typical of the Slate industry. Not large by North Wales standards, never particularly financially strong, they succeeded in outlasting many of their competitors.

BRAICH GOCH SH748079 (19) & GAEWERN SH745086 (14)

A lease of 1787 from John (later Sir John) Edwards, who held the land from the Vanes Estate, to David Williams for 7 years at £38 per year for the whole of Gaewern & Braich Goch, conferred mineral and quarrying rights but this may have been a standard form of land lease rather than an indication that working had or was about to commence. There was working in 1812 as G. Pugh was

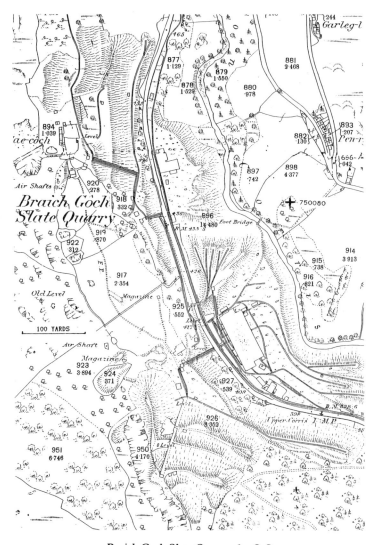

Braich Goch Slate Quarry, 1st O.S.
By kind permission National Library of Wales.

killed by a rockfall. The first known lease specifically relating to commercial quarrying was in February 1834 when Hugh Lloyd, leased Gaewern farm for 40 years at a rent of £100 per five years. William Owen, occupier, of the farm, being paid £2 per year for any inconvenience quarrying caused. Within months Lloyd granted an underlease to George Baker of Tŷ'n y Ceunant, who had already been working the Rhognant section of Gaewern.

The rent on this underlease was ridiculous, £880 for the first 5 years, £1250 for the next 5, then £1000 for each quinquenial, up to the final 4 years, 1870-74 of £880. Baker clearly did not intend to pay these unrealistic sums, for the following February (1835), the lease was reassigned to John Henry Howard and William Prosser, who paid Lloyd £900 for his trouble, plus agreeing £100 per 2 years, additional rent. In December that same year the lease was again re-assigned to Robert Higgins, Joseph Allen Higgins, Congreve Selwyn and Francis Hooper, who were, with Baker, putting together the Merionethshire Slate Company. The company paid Baker the rather large sum of £3197 for the "Machine House" which he had erected.

In 1836, not content with their Gaewern speculation, this same quintet joined J.H. Rowlands in forming the North Wales Slate & Slab quarry, to develop next door at Braich Goch. The lease, again from Edwards, was for 40 years at £50 per year merging to a tenth Royalty on the output. They undertook not to obstruct Gaewern's workings and to keep 10 men employed. This minimum workforce clause was common during the earlier years of the 19th C to ensure that lessees got on with generating royalties, but usually proved unenforceable.

Immediately 8 Bargains were let, soon increasing to 14. Most bargains were paid about £20 per 4 week month, before stoppages for candles, gunpowder, tools etc. but some got much less. Separate costs are shown for smith's shop, rubblers, planers and slab dressers. They produced a wide range of roofing slates, including moss slates and ton slates. Also Slab and headstones (the latter carrying a surcharge to cover the additional sawing). In 1837 their Cost Book included an item for 20 tons of sand 1/[5p] per ton suggesting sand saws were used.

Things certainly seemed to be moving here at Braich Goch, for in 1838 a lot more land was taken. Starting at £50 per year, the rent for it was to increase each 7 years to reach £100 at the end of the 50 year lease. Plus, later in the year, some more ground at £20 pa. All these rents merged to a one-tenth royalty. It is interesting that this was also an underlease from Sir John Edwards, who had recently been increasing his Vanes estate holdings, presumably in shrewd anticipation of events and in fact was being described as a "slate proprietor".

Mention was made of a Machine House erected by Francis Hooper, presumably he had already been working there. In 1840 the building of an incline on this new land was recorded.

Meanwhile at Gaewern, it is not clear if any of the enormous rent due to Lloyd was actually paid. By the end of 1838 matters were in disarray, the original 5 dropped out and J.H. Rowlands in association with William Hughes, reconstituted the company under an unchanged name, with a new 48 year lease, at a realistic rent of £20 pa merging to one tenth the value of slate raised. In June 1844, Hughes having dropped out, Rowlands had the lease transferred to himself, and 2 years later, was joined by Frank Howard and John Bright, with David Davies as manager.

Meanwhile at Braich Goch also, things were not going well. In 1843 the company surrendered the lease, on payment of £50 penalty, and passed the lot, including "Building, Mills & Wheels" to Arthur Coulston, a Civil Engineer. He was granted a new lease, direct from the Vanes estate, for 54 years at a rent for the first 7 years of £50, increasing to £65, then at 7 year intervals to £75, £85, & £95, and for the remainder of the lease, £110, merging to the usual tenth Royalty. There was again a restraint on interfering with Gaewern and at least 8 men were to be "continuously and diligently" employed.

By 1848 Braich Goch were listing 18 x 9s (Viscountesses) at 45/ (£2.25) per mille, 16 x 8s (Ladies) at 30/ (£1.50) per mille & Moss slates at 15/ (75p) per ton. They also were doing considerable Slab business at 4d (1.7p) per foot for 1½" and 3½d (1.46p) per foot for 1¼". They also sold chimney pieces as sets of a slab and 2 "slips". These roofing slate prices were some 20% higher than when Coulston took over, but the Slab prices of about 33/6 (£1.675) per ton were less buoyant. Sales were being made both from the quarry and from the wharf.

Carters carried product to the "Wharf", this being described as at Machynlleth (not at Derwenlas) for which a rent of £4.00 per annum was paid to Jones & Morgan. The usual cartage charge was 5/ (25p) per load, probably about half a ton. Coal brought back as a return load, and sold in the village, provided a small but useful revenue. Some carters like Humphrey Richards, dealt in Slate products in a small way to supplement their takings.

Already enamelling was being done on site and some sales of equipment, such as incline rollers were being supplied to smaller quarries.

In 1850 they were budgeting for new plant, considering spending £95 for a planing machine or £230 for a 'Large planer'. The cost of a saw being put at £35.00.

However over at Gaewern matters were not so prosperous. In 1848 the Merionethshire Slate Company was in dire trouble, and there was a Sheriff's sale. The company ceased trading, but due to difficulties in ascertaining the whereabouts both of E.W. Morris, the Chairman, and West, the Secretary it was not until early 1851 that the winding up proceedings could start. The books were described as "defective" even so, Morris had (unsuccessfully) demanded £350 from the court for their surrender.

Since there was a shortfall of assets over debts (including wages due), with subscribers liable for the difference, many showed an understandable reluctance to come forward. In fact some when traced, repudiated all knowledge of the company. J.W. Rowlands and E.R. Rowlands, son and brother respectively of John Rowlands denied they were shareholders. The Rev. Dr Lamb the elderly vicar of Battle, and his son the Rev. D.T. Lamb both denied that they had authorised the other son, E.A. Lamb to buy shares in their name. At the time of the examination, of the 84 subscribers listed, only 17 had been traced and proved.

It was alleged that the company had only been started by Rowlands in order to unload his quarries. The conduct of all concerned was described as reckless, extravagant and unbusinesslike, if not fraudulent, and "disgraced the history of joint-stock companies".

Notwithstanding the above, John Rowlands got hold of the lease and having picked up some bargains at the sale, — e.g. a "Water wheel & Mill" @ £80, 5 "saws" for £60, 2 "Hand Tables" (Hand powered saws?) for £6, 3 Planing machines for £58 and, oddly, a "pair of hand saws" for £3, went back into business on his own account as the Gaewern Slate Quarry Company.

Immediately there was a scheme, doubtless proposed by Rowlands, that the "North Wales Slate Co." should be formed to take over Gaewern, described as being of 100 acres extent.

Apparently the "present proprietor" (Rowlands) was willing to accept shares to the value of £50,000 and to generously forgo interest until 15% had been paid. "Idris" quarry, an insignificant digging to the northeast of Cader Idris was to be thrown into the deal as makeweight.

Inevitably this fell through but in 1853 Rowlands got Alltgoed Consols, (another of his companies) to take over Gaewern, much against the wishes of some shareholders who doubted, the estimate of 8% return per 6 months predicted by Rowlands' son, J.W. who, having apparently cleared up any misunderstanding with his father over the Merionethshire shares, was acting as manager.

At an Alltgoed Consols meeting in June 1853 it was stated that the fall at Bargain 3 was being cleared, 19 was now producing, 12 was being "roofed", the driving of "18 level" was nearly at an end and that 4,8,10 & 24 were all producing. Sales in June were said to total £600, (including Ratgoed, the other quarry they owned?) and but for the fall and a scarcity of water would have been greater. A 50% increase in the next 6 months was promised.

Meanwhile at Braich Goch, Coulston had clearly become anxious at the now falling prices and in 1851 had got Robert Jackson, William Rees (Architect) & William Wingate (builder), all of Gloucester together with Thomas Wakeman of Chalfont St. Giles to join him in forming the Braich Goch Slate and Slab Company, to buy out the quarry, on which they claimed, £3,000 had been spent, developing 5 "Galleries".

They announced their intention to expand, under the advice of St. Pierre Foley, Inspecting Engineer. Foley said that in the last 3 months 53,400 slates (almost half Duchesses and Countesses) had been made as well as 115 tons of Slab. New bargains were to be let and new workmen's dwellings would be built as some had to walk 8-10 miles to work. According to him, profits on cost had, in the last 3 years averaged 49%. He commended his own proposal to spend £7,034 which, he asserted would enable 100 men to produce an annual profit of £6,518. Even £5,000 spent would enable the number of men to be doubled and provide extra machinery. Apparently "no quarry could offer more favourable capabilities for making vast returns on a moderate scale of expenditure, nor present more legitimate resources for safe and profitable investment."

That August, Nicholls, the Superintendant, announced that lead had been found on 5 Level, but there was never any further mention of this. By November it was predicted that 100 men would be employed on the 111 acre site, that slates to the annual value of £13,500 would be raised with a profit of £7,500 as well as 15,600 tons of Slab which would show a further profit of £12,000. Since such an output would be about 7 times what 100 men could be expected to produce, it is not surprising that, at the end of the year they were still advertising a "few" unsold shares.

In 1852, it was announced that the quarry had, in the past 6 months produced 93,100 slates, about a quarter being Duchesses as well as 73 tons of Slab, and had shown a profit of £264 on sales of £760, a far cry from their predictions of the previous year. However a new Vein of "Fine grain and colour, ½ mile long and 20-25 yards thick" had apparently been discovered. The original quartet were joined by Phillip Johnson, (probably a Slate Merchant) also of Gloucester, and were still offering shares in the "recently formed" company. They reported that No.1 was producing good block, No. 2 had completed opening and new Bargains were producing Duchesses, No. 3 was opening, No. 4 was still "very productive" and No. 5 the "Great Slab Division" was fully maintaining its character".

With the flotation a flop and the plans for a tramway to the Dyfi stalled, the £4,000 John Rowlands put up in 1853 to take it off their hands was welcomed. The plant he took over included a "Water Mill (Williams & Hills patent), 2 waterwheels, 6 planing machines, 9 sawing "engines", 2 miles of tramway and an "inclined plane", 6 hand sawing machines and buildings for enamelling work which included dipping rooms, ovens, showroom and workshop. Oddly only one weighing machine is listed.

Although prices were firming and by 1855 were at an historic high, Rowlands was clearly not profiting from his investment, being, on occasions, unable to meet the men's wages.

Indeed in 1856 he was also having considerable trouble with his

Alltgoed company. Acrimonious meetings were held, worthy shareholders wrote to the press, criticising his running of Ratgoed, so Rowlands agreed to concentrate production at Gaewern, and the next year the Gaewern lease was renewed by the Vanes estate.

At Braich Goch, Rowlands soldiered on, but by 1859 annual tonnage was down to 597 and falling.

Then, in 1864, The Birley family, realising the potential offered by the newly opened tramway, bought Rowlands out, got the lease re-assigned and set up the Braich Goch Slate Quarry Ltd, putting that quarry, at last, on a sound financial footing.

Not so at Gaewern, in 1863 in a re-hash of the 1850s scheme, the Cader Idris Slate & Slab company were to take over the quarry including "3 water-wheels of 20' x 3'6", 18' x 2' & 12' x 4', 7 circular saws, 2 planers", paying £45,000 cash plus £1500 in shares. This fell through and the Alltgoed company having departed the scene, Rowlands, by 1868 got the Talyllyn Slate Company to take it on.

In 1868 the Birleys, apparently prospering at Braich Goch, with well over 200 men, were quoting W.T. Rogers of the Slate & Marble works, Aber, near Bangor, for slab at 70/ (£3.50) per ton 3' - 8' long (thickness unstated) but noted that he required "precise sizes". By this time Slab was invariably being sold by the ton, rather than by square footage. Their price lists showed thicknesses from ½" or ¾" — 2" in 3 groups of dimensions, e.g. 2'6" — 5' x 1'6" — 3', 5' — 7' x 2' + & 7' + x 3' +. In the first group the thinnest would cost 60 - 70% more than the thickest, in the second 35% and the third, 25 — 30%. There was a surcharge for exact sizes.

In 1869 Edwin Williams replaced Richard Williams as clerk/agent at Braich Goch, leaving him to deal with, a slightly amusing dispute, which may have been the reason for the new appointment. Mr Peace of W.T. & J.A. Charles, Sheffield, had in March 1868, on his quarterly visit to the area, taken an order for 36 off 30" diameter saws @ 37/6 (£1.87) each. Apparently offering a substantial discount as the invoice only totalled £55 15 0 (£55.75).

Unfortunately when Ellis Jones the engineer set the saws the teeth broke off and when he recut the teeth, the same thing happened.

On his next visit in June the traveller agreed that the saws were too hard but demanded payment in full, suggesting an "allowance against the next order". This must have seemed acceptable for he came away with a useful order for 30 dozen "double blunt" 10½" files (for saw sharpening) @ 10/4 (52p) per dozen.

However this time the iron was not hard enough, for the files were found to be useless and what is more the allowance of £8 15 0 (£8.75) against the saws seems to have been considered derisory, and to compound the offence, an overcharge of 2/6 (12.5p) on the files invoice was alleged. When the redoubtable Mr Peace made his next quarterly call, not only did he refute the complaints, but he actually came away with a further order for 24 dozen files! These too were unsatisfactory, and after months of correspondence, the matter finished up in court.

In 1876 they were again in dispute. A cargo loaded on the Kohinor of Aberdyfi for J. & J. Cooke of Londonderry failed to arrive at that port. Where it went we do not know.

Early in 1877 yet another firm, the Gaewern Slate Quarry Company Ltd was formed to take over Gaewern (and Tŷ'n y Berth), William Hughes remaining as manager. By 1879 they were employing 80 men producing 1607 tons, having bought a further part of Rhognant ground from a Trevor Evans.

Braich Goch still appeared to be doing well, in 1878 employing almost 280 men, 40 up on the previous year, producing over 7000 tons. In 1880 Edwin Williams had a further lawsuit, this time with the newly steamed Corris Railway, over their claimed right to use C.R. main line themselves, they won but the court warned them against running their own trains beyond Maespoeth in future. Since this would involve horse/gravity working amongst steam services, the court's concern was obvious, but it was several years before the dispute was finalised.

Later that year trade was described as good with stocks running down, but in fact they only produced a little over 5000 tons and had cut their workforce to under 200.

At Gaewern, the new company there was having greater problems, for in 1880 their tonnage was halved to 828 and their manning cut to 33. They replaced William Hughes with C.L. Morgan and slapped a writ on the former for £50 19 6 (£50.97), for rent allegedly collected, but not handed over, plus a rather cheeky claim for £200 damages. Hughes brought a cross action claiming to have been owed £97 salary, £29.16.9 (£29.84) in wages that he had paid out,and £15 expenses he had incurred. In 1881, the court found in Hughes' favour, but only to the extent of £66, but this was enough to break the company.

Although trade was even worse in 1880 at Braich Goch, their workforce scarcely reaching 150, the Birleys boldly stepped in, took over the Gaewern lease and in 1882 obtained from the Vanes estate a new lease on the whole property at £200 pa merging with a Royalty of 1/16. This new lease included the 8 Babilon cottages, the 2 at Tyclap, Gaewern cottage, occupied by the manager, and another cottage nearby, the 4 at Glanderi and another 2 pairs nearby, 3 cottages and a cattle building at Gaewern Uchaf, 2 at Caecoch and Caecoch farm. Thus creating a combined unit with an output that year of 5858 tons with 187 men.

There clearly were problems with this expansion, as in spite of upping manning to 250, tonnage fell over the next few years and by 1892 they had had to cut back again to under 150. 1893 brought better results output reaching 6335 tons with a workforce of only 180 or so (a not discreditable 34 tons per man/year).

In spite of this apparent prosperity, there was a running battle to get royalties and carriage reduced. Between 1873 and 1896, they got a consultant J.S. Hughes to produce 9 reports for onward transmission to the Vanes estate, and presumably also the Corris Railway, describing the shortcomings and difficulties of working the quarries.

The 1873 report was a general complaint about hard times, which of course did get better, but the 1881 report written at a time when prices were 25% below the 1876 peak, was more specific, stating that rock was unprofitable on the lower floors. The cost of working floor 6 was 34/ (£1.70) per ton with fixed costs of 20/ (£1) yet the value of the product after deducting a 10% discount was only 52/ (£2.60).

They were not best pleased with their Gaewern acquisition, for the 1882 report, cited the "rude manner" in which that quarry had been worked and said that the works could only be used for ventilation, and expressed the hope that the proposed work to the westward would prove remunerative and that it was only of value in conjunction with Braich Goch. It also stated that Slab, particularly in less profitable large sizes, was an increasing proportion of the output.

In the 1887 report, "adverse elements" were mentioned such as the Vein only being 14 yards wide, against the 20-40 yards at Blaenau Ffestiniog and the 40-120 yards at Nantlle. The 1889 report stated that to work more bargains they would have to drive levels 5 & 6 below the existing northern bargains in Gaewern and the southern bargains in Scwd.

In 1890 Hughes listed the problems in detail — 1) Narrowness of Vein, 2) Scarcity of foot-joints, 3) Frequency of "Crych" and seams of spar, 4) Low yield, 5) Low proportions of 1st qualities, 6) Comparatively small production, 7) High carriage, 8) Poor prices, 9) Depression in the industry.

In 1892 he said "there has been in the previous 5 years, no improvement until Sgwd is reached, where the rock is better but the colour poorer than Blaenau".

The 1896 report is very full, pointing out that untopping and driving were the same regardless of the width of the Vein. Also how in places such as Blaenau, several veins could be worked together, reducing cost. It alleged the scarcity of foot-joints, the frequency of "Crych" and seams of spar compared unfavourably with Blaenau where, it was said, the yield was 1-6 or 1-8 (proportion of product to rock removed) compared with their 1-11. Their proportion of slate to slab was 1-3½ compared with 1-2½ or 1-3 elsewhere. They had to make fewer Firsts and more Mediums and Seconds than either Blaenau or Nantlle, averaging £2 4 0 (£2.20) against Blaenau's £3 2 0 (£3.10) and the Nantlle's £2 15 0 (£2.75), and that their 'small" production of 5000 tons was to their disadvantage. (Their prices were in fact better than they had been getting for some years, but the steep premium that those other areas could obtain must have riled). High carriage charges were also cited. They had to pay 3/- (15p) per ton for inland sales and 5/9 (27p) by sea whereas Blaenau only paid 10d (4p) for material loaded on rail at the town and 1/10 (9p) loaded at Minfford, or 2/1½ (10.5p) for shipping. Nantlle paid 2/ (10p) in all cases.

Hughes did grudgingly admit that after 18 years, there has been some improvement in the industry, but claimed that their quarries were now "worked out except for the north end of Gaewern and that any further development must be downwards".

Getting down to figures he cites a "large quarry" on a 60 year lease where 2/6 (12.5p) was paid in royalties with 1/6 (7.5p) on "inferior slate". Another, Merionnydd property was paying 2/ (10p) per ton on 16 x 8 (Ladies) and 1/ (5p) for smaller sizes. Both these were working best quality Veins, worth 35% more than Gaewern slate, were 30% more productive and that they did not have the burden of 500%? dearer carriage to rail or 150% dearer carriage to port. An ad valorem royalty of 1/40 was proposed.

Besides these reports, in 1888 they joined with Abercwmeiddaw and Aberllefenni in complaining of both the Corris and the Cambrian Railways' "unreasonable" handling charges of 2/6 (12.5p) per ton.

Problems of non-payment were frequent at this time, mostly they did eventually get paid after their solicitors pursued the debt, but in 1887, having ignored an order for 5000 16 x 8 seconds from Biddulph Valley Mercantile Co (presumably for the obvious reason), the customer threatened to seek damages for non-supply!

In 1892 Leases on both quarries were surrendered and a fresh joint lease taken, at unchanged terms. That year they were selling mediums 18 x 9 @ 87/6 (£4.375) & Seconds @ 65/- (£3.25) less 10 %, plus 1/ (5p) for loading on rail for a Norwich customer. Oddly, the year before on a fairly substantial order from Worcester for 500 24 x 12 Best @ 232/6 (£11.62), 100 20 x 10 Medium @ 130/ (£6.50) and 1000 18/9 Seconds @ 65/ (£3.25) they only allowed 7½% discount. In the same year 5 "Billiards tables", weighing 17 cwt each, @ 75/- (£3.75) plus 10d (4p) loading per ton, were sold to Dublin (Rail to Holyhead).

Also in 1892 1T 7cwt 2qt of "Tombstones" were sent to Ilfracombe, priced at 70/ (£3.50) per ton along with 2 Tons of "Sills" @ 50/ (£2.50) loading was charged 1/ (5p) and "Extra work", 2 days @ 5/ per day.

The Merionedd Mines Enquiry of 1892/3 listed them as having 58 men underground and 90 above ground producing 6044 tons, their lowest adit being shown as 390' (No 3?).

By 1896 they were back up to 180 men, but output and manning fell in the last years of the century. In 1902 the 130 men produced a useful 5867 tons, much of it Slab, going to customers such as the Aberystwyth Enamelled Slate & Marble Co. Moor St., Aberystwyth.

Financially, the picture was less rosy, they were shifting the rock but not making money.

Back in the good old days of 1877 sales had totalled £33,671, which after paying wages of £14,330 and meeting other costs of £6,485 left a profit of £12,856. (It is notable that £200 of that profit came from the sales of candles, powder and fuse to the employees!) The following year sales edged up to £34,431, and even with a wage bill of £16,774 showed a profit of £12,319. However the next year, 1879, with prices falling, their sales took a tumble to £20,402 and in spite of having cut their wage bill to £14,730, their profit dived to £4,610.

Worse was to follow, in 1880 their sales were down to £18,000, but by cutting their payroll to £12,393 they just scraped a profit of £586. 1881 saw sales down to under £16,000, which despite wages of only £8,788 showed a loss of £617. In 1882 the acquisition of Gaewern brought a slight improvement in sales, even with a further drop in prices, and the loss was contained at £291.

In 1883 sales slid to under £13,000 but they managed a slim profit of £264. Losses mounted in the following years of the century, in spite of a sharp increase in prices in the early 1890s.

The price hike of 1903 & 1904, brought about by the Penrhyn stoppage did help but a big fall of rock in 1903 cut output. With a reduced workforce, they managed a profit of around £2,000 on sales of £15,000. Over the next 3 years prices fell back, by 1905 their sales were only £9,690, their workforce was cut to around 110 and their profit was a slim £500. In 1906 sales were down to under £6,000, which scarcely covered the wages bill for their 100 men and the stock levels had increased from 2 weeks to 4 months. In spite of creative accounting, a loss of over £1,000 was recorded.

There had been other financial problems. During the early 1890s the executors of the late Edmund Birley had demanded the repayment of substantial loans and other monies due from the company. The payment of these, though resisted by the family, with heavy legal costs, eroded their capital base.

There was correspondence in 1905 between Edwin Williams and the directors as to how the quarry might be profitably worked. Apparently Williams disagreed with the Birleys' proposal of development below Braich Goch, favouring the Hughes of Porthmadoc recommendation to sink below level 5 (Rhognat series?), at Gaewern and at Sgwd. The Birleys were adamant that there was insufficient money for this more expensive alternative.

In one letter, of November 1905, Williams obliquely, but sourly, observed that had not "thousands of pounds" been taken by the directors as "loan interest", funds would have been available.

In the meantime the Birley's were again pressing for a reduction in royalties, payment of which was much in arrears. Hawthorn Birley, having no luck with the Estate Agent, made a direct appeal to Lady Londonderry, who replied expressing her regret at their present difficulties and her "confident expectation that they would be able to resolve them". She made no offer that might assist in that direction! In 1905 the landlords were informed that they might be seeking to surrender the lease as "they were unable to carry on profitable production".

In the 30 years wages costs (at substantially similar rates of pay) had gone from 42% of sales to 92% and general costs from 20% of sales to 45%.

In 1906 the problems were recognised as terminal and the Braich Goch Slate Quarry Company was wound up.

There exists a letter from the quarrymen to the Directors, on what they tactfully describe as their "retirement as owners". It fulsomely and at length acknowledges their "many kindnesses' as employers, the greatest and most notable "kindness" apparently being that wages were regularly paid!

When the Birleys ceased operations, the estate seized the whole quarry and put it on the market at £4,000 plus Stock & Plant at Valuation. A George White did show some interest, but when he dropped out there were no other takers, nor were efforts to sell piecemeal successful.

There then appeared on the scene, Evan Reese, now recovered from his Dulas Enamelling debacle. (Section 8) He had taken an option on Era quarry and, with a whole new generation of folk to borrow from, was again getting ambitious. As soon as the quarry had closed he had expressed an interest in taking over the lease, and indeed he, in 1906, secured an agreement for a new lease at only 1/25th Royalty but with a Dead Rent of £300 which would increase to £500 pa after 5 years. There was a valuation of £1,500 on the plant the main items of which were —

Engine house 1 Steam Engine and Donkey Pump, 1 Lancaster (sic) boiler, 22' x 7' diameter, with 2 flues, 1 ditto 24' x 6' diameter.

Fitting Shop 1 Punching Machine, 1 Small lathe, 1 Drilling Machine, 2 Vices, 1 Bellows, 1 Anvil, 4 Dressing Knives also Fitters & Smiths Tools, Cylinder & Engine Oil and Cast steel and assorted Iron.

Machine House 42 Saws, 3 Planers, 11 Rotary Dressing Machines & 8 Treadle Dressers. A total of over 670′ of shafting from 4½″ down to 2″ diameter, with 250 pulleys in all, and various belting from 5½″ down to 2½″ wide. There were 8 Overhead Travelling Cranes, 4 Self-acting Saw Sharpening Machines. 1 Grindstone & Frame, 16 Wheelbarrows and finally just one stove.

Vanes "Depth" 1700 Yards of Iron Rail (850 yards of tramway), 350′ & 320′ of 1 1/4″ and 350′ of 1″ Wire Rope. A "Drum" 11′ 2″ x 17′ 9″ and another 9′ 5″ x 18′ 10″, the latter with a "double brake band". (These drum sizes are curious particularly as, in each case, the second figure is shown as diameter). After listing 2 Cranes "for loading slate" complete with Chains and Blocks, the schedule then becomes even more curious. 1 Tank of 4′ 9″ gauge, another of 4′ 3″ gauge and a Ballast Waggon of 2′ 2″ gauge and another of 2′ 7″ gauge. It also showed a Weighing Machine, another "at Scwd" and a third at "8 Depth".

A Drum of 10′ 8″ x 24′ diameter (?), a "Double P" Crane and a Stone Cistern are noted as being at 4 Depth.

5 Depth 20 ladders of from 8′ to 45′ 3783 Yards of Rails (1891 yards of tramway), 6 Powder Chests, 5 "Double P" Cranes, complete with Chains, 7 Blocks, 1 "Pudley" Weight (sic) bridge, to weigh 10 tons, 1 Cast iron Drum with centre brake band, 172′ of 1″ & 186′ of 1 1/4″ Wire Rope and a ballast tram.

6 Depth 5 Powder Chests, 7 "Double P" Cranes, 16 ladders 8′ — 34′, 6823 Yards of Rail (3411 yards of tramway), 1 Weighing Machine, 1 Ditto, Hudson & Stead to weigh 5 tons, 14 Iron Trams, 52 Block Cars, 6 Slab Cars, 36 Slate Trams, 2 Wooden Wagons, 27 Turntables, 3 Rail Turners (points?) and "Several hundred yards" of workmen's chains, "in the Bargains".

Store Room 1 Tarpaulin, 1 Wooden Stand, (could this be a trimming stool?) Wagon Oil, an unspecified number of 30″ & 24″ circular saws, 14 "plates" of glass, 1 Hydraulic Column, 7 Powder Bottles, 2 Smith Bellows, 1 Cupboard, 3 Lamps, 1 Oil Can, 4 Slate Dressing Knives, a "few dozen" assorted files, ¼ hundredweight of Rivets, some Brasses and Castings, 1 bundle of Fencing Wire, 1 Bar of Iron, 6 Oil Taps, 7 old Window Frames.

Carpenter's Shop 2 Benches, 2 Water Pipes and Shoe, 1 old Window Frame, 9 Explosives Chests, 1 1/2 sets (sic) of Steel Wheels with Fixed Axles, 1 old Screw Jack, 4 Steel Wheels, some Hoop Iron and a quantity of Old Iron, 1 Pit-saw, 3 Circular Saws, 1 Cross-cut Saw, 1 pressing clamp, 1 Saw Sharpening Stand, 1 Vice.

Old Smithy 1 Smith's Bellows, 1 Anvil, 2 Iron Stands, 1 Weighing Machine, 4 Bars of Iron, 1 Iron Cistern, 1 Stone ditto, 2 Tram Shafts, Iron Moulds, 5 Tongs, 2 Cupboards, a small Chest, and a quantity of Old Iron.

Outside Smithy 7 old Wheels, 1 old Tram Frame, 14 Bars of Iron.

Old Air-compressor House 18 new Fire-bars for boilers, quantity of old Brasses etc, 70 firebricks, 80' of Rope, 1/2 sheet of Copper 1/2 sheet of Tin, 27 Bars of assorted Iron, 40 x 56lb weights (1 Ton), 1 Patent Block & Chain, 1 Screw Jack, some Wire Rope.

The list was completed with an inventory of office chairs, desks etc.

Evan Reese seemingly never actually got round to signing the lease or buying the plant, but in early 1908 came out with an astonishing offer to buy the whole of the Braich Goch & Gaewern estate for £32,500, backing it with a £1,500 option. Besides the quarries a large number of dwellings were included. The Braich Goch and the Gaewern farms, let @ £45.00 & £20.00, respectively. "Shops" let at £24, and the Braich Goch Hotel at the same figure. Brynderi, Gaewern & Caecoch let at, respectively, £12.00, £10.00 & £8.10.0 (£8.50). The 6 cottages of Braich Goch Terrace @ £6.10.0 (£6.50) each & the 4 at Babilon, 8 at Glanderi, 2 at Caecoch as well as Gaewern Isa at £4.6.8 (£4.33 each. Also Frongoch & the 3 Tyros cottages @ £3.5.0 (£3.25), there were sundry other rents including the "Corris Railway Water Supply" (at Maespoeth), @ £1 & Corris Baptist Chapel @ 10/- (50p).

The reason for this astonishing offer was that Van de Bruga Villa, an obscure figure with quarrying experience in France, was putting together backing to form the General United Slate Company Limited, and was looking for somewhere to dig. Reese had got the company's agreement in principle to buy Braich Goch, Gaewern and Era quarries for £50,000. This would have shown him a considerable profit and left him with a useful rent-roll.

Unfortunately General United intended to pay not in cash, but in shares. The most they would agree to in ready money was £2,000 deposit. Since the total funds of the company at the time appears to have been the £1 each of the 5 directors subscribed, the £2,000 was not forthcoming, and the deal, shortly afterwards fell to bits.

To add to Reese's problems the Vanes Estate were claiming dead rent from him, as option holder. He owed sums to several banks and a number of local persons whom he had touched for loans. His credit ran out, his cheques were dishonoured and by the end of the year he was bankrupt, owing almost £3,000. Eventually he paid out 7/6 (37.5p) in the pound.

The estate once again took possession. In 1910, G.F. Wright who was trying to run Llwyngwern quarry, after all the plant there had been sold from under him, made an (unsuccessful) application to Lord Vane-Tempest to "borrow" the still idle Braich Goch machinery.

In 1912 an attempt was made to form the Braichgoch and Rhognant Slate Quarries Ltd, to take over the Braich Goch, Gaewern and, surprisingly, Bryn Llwyd quarries. This latter being included as the redoubtable Evan Reese was still around and still trying to unload this dud property.

The whole was described as being of 900 acres, having ample gathering ground for water for power and electric light and capable of raising 100 tons of slate per day. And, at dead rent of £100 pa, without royalty, clearly a snip.

In spite of a whole raft of "experts" making favourable comments suggesting 100 years supply of reserves, with costs predicted to average 42/ - 45/ (£2.10—£2.25) per ton and revenues 60/ - 70/ (£3.00 -3.50) per ton, the flotation flopped, and soon the war put paid to any further ventures.

In early 1919, in spite of the post-war boom, there seemed such little prospect of a resumption that Lord Vane-Tempest, allowed H. Brown of Sheffield to take away 3,000 yards of rail on a 12 months hire for £90.00. However later that year Cadwaladr Humphries and T.O. Williams, took leases and options on Braich Goch (and Abercorris) and re-started work, anticipating the floating of the Welsh Slate Combine.

This grand scheme had as its Board-designate, a General and a Lieutenant General (both knighted), Alderman W.J. Parry from

Bethesda and Cadwalader Owen Roberts J.P. (who owned the New Welsh Slate Company at Cwt y Bugail, Blaenau Ffestiniog), T.O. Williams, was to be general manager. This £300,000 investment opportunity was to pay Roberts £45,000 for his quarry (£15,000 in cash, the rest in shares). For Braich Goch, Gaewern, Rhognant and Abercorris, Humphries and Williams were to receive £75,000, £25,000 to be in hard cash.

The Prospectus included extracts from a report by an R.M. Roberts, who said that Braich Goch was turning a considerable monthly output of Slates and Slabs, which found a ready sale. (No figures were quoted!). Reserves were estimated at 76 million tons, which allowing for a third for pillaring and a 1 to 6 make-to-waste ratio gave a saleable potential of 8 million tons. This was translated at £8 per ton into a potential yield of £64,000,000! Additionally the 15-20 million tons in the waste dumps were cited as a source of crushed material, asserting that enquiries had been received for the purchase of 3-500,000 tons pa which, it was darkly hinted, would yield a "considerable profit".

Roberts estimated a life of 250 years, "assuming an annual output of 200,000 tons". A figure somewhat at variance both with his optimistic estimate of reserves and the fact that very few quarries had ever got within sight of a tenth of that output. He admitted that electric power would be required but this was estimated as "not above £8,000".

The Braich Goch mill was described as exceptionally well arranged and equipped and capable of dealing with heavier work than is generally the case. The weighbridges, rolling stock, the mile of railroad and all the winches, chains, ladders and tools were apparently in "splendid" condition.

His valuation of plant and buildings was £60,000 and the 4000 yards of tunnelling and underground tramway at £10 a yard to be worth £40,000. (Some 67 times the valuation of a dozen years earlier!)

Detailed costs per ton followed — Royalties 6/6 (32p), Carriage 2/6 (12.5p), Wages £4.00, Coal 1/11 (10p), maintenance 3/10 (19p) and "other items" 1/11 (10p) which at his estimate of £8.00 per ton gave a profit of £3 3 4 (£3.16). He estimated the annual profit at the rather precise figure of £69,666 13 4, based on "only 500" men being employed, they producing 22,000 tons pa (a very optimistic 44 tons per man!).

There were few, if any, takers for this "unique investment opportunity", and failing to unload, Williams and Humphries were joined by T. Edwards in 1921, in setting up the Corris Slate & Slab Quarry Ltd. with E. Griffiths as manager, and were soon employing about 60 men.

They struck trouble straight away. Following the 1919-1920 bonanza, prices had fallen, earnings were down so that wages on bargains scarcely exceeded "daily rates" and management throughout the industry sought to reduce these "fall-back" scales. Although the proposed cut here of 2/6 (12.5p) per day was less than say, the Blaenau cut of 3/- (15p), in October 1921 there was a strike which lasted almost 3 months before the men had to accept the inevitable and go back.

By the mid 1920's they were employing over 100, but by 1929, they had to cut back to around 70, with Edwards taking over the management himself.

In 1931 B.T. Jones of Blaenau Ffestiniog, bought them out, forming the Braich Goch Slate & Slab Quarry Ltd, shortly afterwards selling out to W. Horton, who owned Rhiw'r Gwreiddyn and who by 1934 had acquired Abercorris where he employed 8 or 9 men in addition to his 100 men at Braich Goch. T. Edwards stayed on to manage the lot. By the outbreak of war although things held up at the small Abercorris operation, at Braich Goch numbers were down to around 60. By the end of the war scarcely 20 remained and even after the war numbers never much exceeded 30.

Sale Particulars in 1951, when following the death of the Marquis of Londonderry, most of the properties in Corris were disposed of, lists Braich Goch Slate & Slab quarry as being let to tenants at £150 pa with 17 years lease to run. The 416 acre site included Gaewern farm sub-let at £20 pa. It mentions that the tenants ran this quarry in conjunction with another adjoining (Abercorris). The property, which was sold before the sale, included a 270' x 100' building with C.G.I. roof, but it was noted that the machinery, as tenants property, was not included. It is of interest that some cottages are described as having a water supply by spring.

Mains electricity was laid on in the early 1950s. In late 1950s a company, Corris Fillers attempted to set up powder making.

In 1962 the quarry was bought by the Lloyd brothers of Aberllefenni from D.H. Tudor the then owner. The Lloyds modernised the mill, but unfortunately much of the best rock which had yielded some very high quality slab in large sizes, was virtually worked out, and they had to concentrate on the then declining electrical panel trade. In 1970 the road improvement scheme came about, the quarry closed and the machines and the few remaining men transferred to Aberllefenni.

Description (Braich Goch)

There was, in the earliest days, a mill on the hillside, above the road, but as expansion took place an extensive mills area was created between the then main road and the river. The main mill was where the present cafe and workshops are (but at about 25 feet lower level) with a boiler house at its northern end, and an office building, later increased to 2-storeys, to the south. The Upper Corris tramway virtually ran through the yard.

The very narrow Appendix Vein was worked from the southern end of Gaewern, almost to a point behind the Braich Goch hotel.

The C.E. Spooner plans of 1867, 1873 & 1882 show there were workings on 7 levels, with no underground inclines. The workings, below 6 Level were later. Since the Vein basically dipped "away" i.e. to the west, the lower the adit, the longer was the run in through the "hard" to reach the bottom of the Vein to establish a strike tunnel.

An adit from 6 Level emerged near the main mill at mill level, with a tramway to the mill. Material from 5 Level adit, some 25 feet above the old road, (which now serves as a service road for the cafeworkshops), crossed that road by a bridge, turned right on the flat top of a tip, to a short incline to the mill. Later a line connected this adit to the 4-6 incline, the bridge only being used for rubbish.

The next level above 5 was Vanes Level, (in a sense a mezzanine between 4 & 5), its adit was some distance to the north. Like the other adit tunnels, it too made a "T" junction onto the strike tunnels, and served the most northerly workings, with the final chambers eventually under Gaewern workings. Originally there was an incline down from the Vanes adit via a reverse, to another road-bridge to give access, via a short incline to the mill area, but later there was a connection overground to the 5 Adit area (shown on the 1901 O.S. map). In the 1950s, this route was made redundant by the construction of an underground incline down to 6 level.

The Level 4 adit was served by the aforementioned 4-6 incline which passed under the old road (at right angles to it), there was a smithy adjacent to 4 adit. There was a further 1-4 incline which ran down diagonally across the ground, in a northerly direction, from the partly open-air upper workings, serving Levels 2 & 3 adits on the way. This incline appears disused on the 1901 O.S. There was open working and much tipping in this area. The total vertical interval between Levels 1 & 6 being about 300 feet. Further to the south was an isolated working, shown as "old level" which may have been a very early trial. The Bryn Llwyd Uchaf level SH748072 is shown on early plans as a "trial".

The surface tramway from Gaewern is shown in 1882 as a proposal, reflecting the amalgamation plans, also shown is Spooner's recommendation for working below 6 Level by "pumping & winding". Around 1890, two levels below 6 were opened up, hauling up to 6 by an underground incline.

Latterly all material went out from 6 adit via the undergound incline down from Vanes level.

Description(Gaewern)

Some working was open, but most was underground.

The older, upper, westerly workings were known as Sgwd, the easterly as Rhognant. The open workings nearer the road, known as "Old quarry" were the early Glanderi workings.

Unusual was the multiple use of hand operated circular saws, probably installed in the 1820s. These fearsome two-man cranked devices were employed singly in several very small quarries but to have more than one, on a larger site was most unusual.

There were eventually, two water powered mills. The upper mill was on the site itself. The second mill was on the eastern side of the main road, water being tandemed from the upper mill, via a small holding pond. It is thought that there was, at one time a steam engine put in, possibly the upper mill, due to water shortage. The O.S. of 1891 shows the Upper Mill but the 1901 does not.

The C.E. Spooner survey of 1882 shows the somewhat confusing numbering of the levels arising from the independent working in early years. 1 Rhognat approximates to 4 Sgwd, but due to varying vertical intervals, 2 (Rhognat) is lower than 5 (Sgwd) and 3

(Rhognat) some 30' below 6 (Sgwd), only 20' higher than 7 (Sgwd). (The lowest Gaewern level, 8 (Sgwd), is 75' above the Braich Goch Vanes level). At the top of the site were, downward from south to north, 1,2,3 & 4 adits, (Sgwd numbers), the latter being close to the Rhognant stream. 1 & 2 (partly open workings) appear as disused on the Spooner plans (a note shows 1 as "Ventilating adit under hard"). From adit 3 a tramway (The "Sgwd" tramway) ran north-east, past the foot of a table incline down from 2, which Spooner in 1882 described as "old incline to be used for lowering blocks from 2 to Sgwd tramway". This was apparently later extended downwards. The line then curved around to the south passing between the upper reservoir and the upper mill, past the 1 (Rhognant) adit to the head of an incline which ran, east, under the main road, to reach the lower mill. At the head of this incline was the 7 (Sgwd) adit and part way down, the 8 (Sgwd) adit fed in from a short tramway. This Sgwd line was extended on the surface to an incline down to Braich Goch, thus enabling block to be taken to Braich Goch mill, rather than using the lower mill here. (This line appears on the 1891 O.S. but on the 1901 O.S. is shown as "disused"). Another Spooner proposal, seemingly never taken up, was to abandon the lower end of the under road incline and connect its new foot south to Braich Goch and north to a rubbish bridge over the road.

From the 4 (Sgwd) adit another line, the Rhognant tramway, led around to the upper mill, behind which was the 2 (Rhognant) adit and beyond, the underground incline down to 4 (Rhognant) which emerged below the main road. This provided a route to the Upper Corris tramway for finished product from the upper mill.

Remains (Braich Goch)

Shortly after closure the southern part of the site was landscaped, obliterating the mills area and all traces of the extensive workings above. However on the northerly part there are traces of workings, some buildings and tramroad formations, including the surface connection to Gaewern. There are some points here where chambering breaks out to bank. There are some 15' lengths of malleable iron T section rail with 5 "fishbellies" probably Upper Corris tramway metal. There are several dwellings on the line of the old main road which were quarry owned.

After landscaping, three adits were retained.

No. 6, at the former mills level was, in latter days, the main exit from underground, serving the now collapsed workings to the south, and chambers to the north. It served the uphaulages from the lower workings and the incline down from Vanes level. At the head of each incline old saw blades acted as signalling gongs. Abandoned were winch mountings, a steam winder (which would have been driven off the compressed air line), a portable lavatory and other minor artifacts.

The No 5 adit, which at one time was connected to the mills area by a bridge over the then main road, has a tunnel towards the southern workings, where a hand winch was abandoned, and northerly to the Vanes-6 incline.

The third adit was Vanes level. This also served the collapsed southerly workings, but mainly serviced the Northenmost chambers. These chambers, the last to be worked, are under, and break into, Gaewern workings, affording, at one time, it is alleged, many an opportunity for an "early finish". A loop of the tunnel leads to the top of the fine, close-timbered incline, down to level 6, single-acting, built around 1950 (in 2 weeks working round-the-clock, by, it is said, candlelight) when extraction was concentrated at the north end of Vanes level.

At closure several artifacts were left in place, including a steam winder, two hand winches, rail & pointwork in situ, part of a channelling machine and a lavatory as well as several minor items.

The present main road craft workshops and cafe are on ground built up on the old mills and stocking area. The trackbed of the Upper Corris Tramway forms a footpath to the east of the main road.

At the time of writing (1993), Level 6, is the location of the proposed Corris Caverns development.

Remains Gaewern

Bulk removal of tip material, creation of access tracks, road widening and time, have made site interpretation difficult.

At the top of the site is the dried-out bed of the upper reservoir, with a slate covered leat leading down to the site of the upper mill. Above is a shaft (Sgwd 1).

Beyond are the open workings of 2 & 3 Sgwd levels with a rubbish run line curving round from 2 level, with traces of a building. The Sgwd tramway parallels below it at 3 level. A table incline with drumhouse in fair condition goes down to the Rhognant tramway below. There are also vestiges of another 2-3 incline and a 3-4 incline.

The line passes prominent traces of the old 1 Adit (Rhognant) and as it leaves the site farm buildings are behind what was the 7 adit (Sgwd), and some possible vestiges of the incline which ran down under the road. Towards Braich Goch it passes the ruins of a powder house. Below, to the left, is the lower reservoir, still holding water and beyond it Gaewern farm. There are slate sleepers in situ. Further on, landscaping has obliterated the line and its incline which ran to near the Braich Goch Vanes level.

At a lower level is the formation of the Rhognant tramway starting at 4 (Sgwd) adit, near which is a weigh-house and from where water emerges from the collapsed open workings. The line passes the foot of the table incline and finishes near the top of the present access track to the site. At the end of the line there is a cleared area that was the site of the upper mill. There is an obvious opening where the incline went down underground, to connect with 4 adit (Rhognant) under the main road. There are traces of the drumhouse masonry. There is no trace of the under road adits.

Underground, there is much chambering on several levels, extending to above the northernmost Braich Goch workings.
The roofs in all these workings are particularly unstable so the warning on trespass and danger is absolute.

Section 4 UPPER CORRIS

The two largest, but very different quarries were on the North-eastern side. Abercwmeiddaw, worked the Broad Vein, and against the odds produced substantial tonnages from it, and in times of high prices at least, brought some financial return.

The other, Abercorris, worked the far better quality narrow Vein. However it was developed too late to benefit from the good times up to the mid 1870's, even so had it been worked with the best skill and foresight, it might not have suffered the financial traumas which beset it for most of its life. Today, considerable reserves of very good quality slate remain, which perhaps will one day be worked.

On the South-western side, the Gaewern boundary represented the limit of really successful working. The two quarries on the narrow Vein, Tŷ'n y Berth & Tŷ'n y Ceunant only produced moderate tonnages. Of those on the Broad Vein, or on outlying occurrences, there was little success. Only one, Cwm Dylluan got beyond the trial stage, but its insignificant output can have provided scant return for the effort expended.

ABERCORRIS SH754089 Locally known as Cwmodyn (27)
A lease of 1863 shows land being let to Thomas Green of London by Humphrey & David Davies. This was not the first work done here, as a report in the Mining Journal in December that year, referred to T. Green and Evan Hopkins, having taken possession of an "old" Corris quarry during the previous April, and that they were making first-class slates and Slab. It described trade as brisk and that more men would be taken on.

Encouraged by the boom conditions in 1874, the Cwmodyn Slate & Slab Quarry Company, was formed, but directly prices started to fall in early 1877, they were in trouble and in March 1878 their mortgagees sold them up by auction.

In 1880 the quarry was described as being "recently opened", apparently by J.W. Orchard. Output was recorded that year but not again until 1883, when the Abercorris Slate and Slab Quarry Ltd was registered with Orchard as M.D. with 45 men employed. They did not fare well in the poor trading conditions then prevailing for in 1886 a cheque to the Corris Railway bounced and slate en-route was impounded. They cut down to 37 men, and in 1888 were forced to close.

In 1889 Edward Lee re-opened and built up to over 40 men, but in 1892, down to only 9 men with the C.R. pressing them for money and reluctant to carry their product, landlord Humphrey Davies seized the stock and plant.

In 1893 W. John Lewis and Arthur T. Carr (of the Towyn, later, Maglona syndicate) took a 40 year lease at £100 pa merging to a 1/18th royalty. They bought the stock and machinery for £2,500 and set up the Abercorris Quarry Co. Ltd, the recovery of prices in the past couple of years apparently encouraging speculation. They took on 35 men but only raised 384 tons in the first year.

In the ensuing years mortgages and debentures were obtained for further working capital and in 1901 a debt to the Maglona Company was transferred to W.J. Lewis personally. The company minute book around this time constantly refers to debt problems and the need for more capital. These problems do not seem to have deterred the Directors from increasing their own fees.

Production in 1902 was 1132 tons, under David Roberts' managership with employment remaining around 40 or so, but by 1907 numbers were down to 15 and by 1909 with employment scarcely in double figures, sales were being made through Lewis's Ratgoed and Cymerau quarries.

Closed in 1914, there was a revival in 1920 when T.O. Williams and C. Humphries, then involved in the Great Welsh Slate combine, did some work. In 1928, following a failure to raise more capital, the Abercorris company was wound up.

There was sporadic working in the 1930s, Horton having taken it on by 1934 and in the early 1950s there was some very limited working in conjunction with Braich Goch, both being owned by D.H. Tudor. Electricity was supplied by the latter's generator, owing to limited power, working was, for a time, confined to 4.00 pm — midnight.

Description

On the Narrow Vein, mainly underground, on several levels, some started as open quarrying developed into pits accessed by tunnels, others by direct aditting, the highest being at over 1000' asl. Material was lowered by the long incline, to a mills area the first mill being water powered, a later and larger mill was steam, then finally electrically driven.

There were some workings above the main incline which were served by a second, shorter incline, one of these, part way down, being the last level to be worked. There were also some trials higher again.

Originally access was by cart track, later by direct connection to the Upper Corris Tramway, via an incline, and a reversing loop to a bridge over the river.

Remains

The big single-pitch table incline is the most prominent feature, 670′ long with a gain of height of almost 400′. Whilst not on the heroic scale found in, say, Cwm Croesor it nevertheless must have been a formidable climb to work at 6 o'clock on a Winter morning.

One adit to a pit has been tipped over, another, leading to underground workings is lost in forestry. One adit on the upper incline is open leading to some chambering, with a shaft for lowering material to the level below. A remote type drumhouse is at the top of the main incline with brakeman's shelter on the crimp. Some rail and rope is on the ground. The upper incline is badly degraded. There is a small reservoir, partway down the main incline, in this are remnants of a wagon which ran away after a rope broke. Surprisingly, the man riding on the wagon was uninjured but the brakeman was hurt by the recoiling rope.

Only traces remain of the original mill. The later mill, which contained 4 saws, a planer and a dresser, has collapsed, nearby is a small ruined building and a hut which was the Caban ("Canteen") for the mill men.

At a lower level, there are an office and dwellings in fair condition. The cottages were abandoned in the 1930's and since it was considered anti-social for the men to come to work without fuel for the Caban fire, the woodwork of these cottages rapidly vanished!

The incline connection down to the Upper Corris tramway is just about traceable in the trees and the abutments of the bridge over the river are obvious.

ABERCORRIS SH752082 (25)

This tiny underground working should not be confused with the

Abercorris quarry proper. It was an unsuccessful trial by Lewis Jones of Penyrallt, virtually in his back garden.

Description

Just a short tunnel.

Remains

A collapsed adit, some spoil.

ABERCWMEIDDAW SH746093 (15)

This was the only quarry in the district to work the Broad vein on anything like a scale, or with any success, if indeed their very mixed fortunes could be so described.

The earliest known reference was in 1849 when the Mining Journal reported that, "Mr Jones' works opposite Tŷ'n y Ceunant, are employing 80 men." The history during 50s & 60s is obscure, but a good deal of work underground was done.

The Landlords, (The Ecclesiastical Commisioners, the Living of Llanfachreth and the Vaughans of Nannau), granted a 60 year lease in the late 1860s at £30 pa dead rent merging with a tonnage royalty of 2/6 (12.5p) for the first 10 years, 3/- (15p) for the next 10, and 3/6 (17.5p) for the next 10, finally, 4/- (20p) for the remainder. To whom is not clear.

When offered for sale in 1871, it was clearly a well established concern, although apparently not yet connected to the Upper Corris Tramway, as a report by John Imray shows.

He described the Vein as being "400 yards wide, a mile long and of unknown depth". He said that it had been "exposed by open cutting, adit tunnels produce large slabs and slate, and are connected by tramway". He praised the situation mentioning "good water supply for most of the year" and the quality of the product, with its "regular fractures and good split. Adits have been machine cut 7' 4" diameter to 150 yards across the vein, and a shorter tunnel and access tunnel with a shaft between levels."

He indicated that connection with "The tramway" (The Upper Corris Tramway) would give a carriage cost of 2/3 (11p) per ton. Among equipment on site that he listed, was a "tunnelling machine", 2 small steam engines, an "undercutting machine", a planer and a double saw.

He suggested that the property could be divided into several quarries or could be worked as one by the installation of additional plant which he priced at — Saws £50, planer £90, Slate cutter (trimmer?), £20, Quarry crane £15, Shop cranes £50, Steam engine & boiler £600 & Trucks @ £7 each.

It was bought by William Bright, who when the Abercwmeiddaw Slate Quarry Ltd. was floated in 1876, sold to them, remaining as managing director. Robert Williams was poached from Bryneglwys to act as manager, but "retired" very shortly afterwards being replaced by G. Taafe. It was classed as a mine.

In 1879 trade was described as "good, with even small sizes selling", and by 1880 they had built up to 130 men, including 6 underground workers, producing 3231 tons and in 1882, 188 men produced 4173 tons, but this was down to 2875 tons in 1883, with a drastically cut workforce of under 80, and reclassified as an open working.

The recession of the mid '80s brought financial difficulties. In 1885 they were seriously behind with their Corris Railway account and shortly afterwards closed for a couple of years.

An attempt was made to sell in 1893, the lease being declared as having been granted in 1869.

The very full description shows that in the past 20 years a considerable amount of plant had been installed.

The 266' x 48' Machine House is described as having "side wings for splitting and dressing, with glass in roof" and with "rails, turntables and cranes, containing 29 saw tables (9' x 5') with 22" saws, 15 two-bladed dressing machines (3' x 2") and 3 treadle dressing machines' (3' 3"). There was, however, still only one planer (8' x 4') listed. The mill cranes were of 2 ton and a 3 ton capacity. Other plant included a horizontal double saw sharpening machine, a powered grindstone, a lathe and a 4' woodsaw. Minor equipment included 2 "hand knives & blocks" (for slate trimming). Other buildings included an 85' x 28' slate store, carpenter's and smith's shops, a stable, hay and straw stores, oil store, a powder house and 6 weighbridges.

Quarry plant included 4 cranes and 2 crab-winches, 51 iron rubbish wagons, 40 block wagons, 1 slab wagon and 14 braked railway wagons.

For power besides the 45' x 3' 6" waterwheel, (complete with 300 yards of troughing), there was a 30hp, 2 cylinder steam engine by Roby of Lincoln, with bore of 12″ & stroke of 18″, complete with 6′ 4″ x 12″ flywheel (For mill driving?). Also, a horizontal winding engine 12″ bore x 24″ stroke of unspecified power, by H. & J. Ellis of Salford, complete with boiler 12′ x 5′. There was also an Ellis locomotive described as "2′ 6″ (?) with multi-tubed boiler. (De Winton pattern).

Listed too, was a "Water balance tank for hauling from the level of sink to machine house, 3 tons capacity". Three inclines, with drums were mentioned as were "3 carriages for trollies on top incline, one with turntable". Also included in the offer were the manager's house, some cottages, a "double office on the second gallery" as well as the contents of the Machynlleth office. Among the small sundries itemised were "a quantity of ferns and rushes for packing". The quarry itself was described as being in "5 galleries, only 2 now worked".

Failing to sell, they soldiered on with a workforce dwindling to 50, but their main product being roofing slate, the Penrhyn dispute, helped them more than most Corris quarries and by 1902 production was up to 2,222 tons, with a workforce of 74. There was a setback in 1903 when they went down to 50 men but in spite of being busy in 1904/5 when they were back up to over 90 men, the subsequent collapse of prices made sales unprofitable and closure came in 1905.

A restart was made in 1911 with the company reformed under the same name, backed by local men such as T. Morris who was a Chemist in Corris, W. Jones who had a shop in Aberdyfi and J.N. Roberts a wholesale grocer from Barmouth, with R. Davies as manager. With a heavy rent it was unprofitable, when war came they discharged their 22 men, liquidating in 1917. Roberts took it on himself restarting in 1919.

With dis-establishment on 1st January, 1920 the Bangor Diocesan Board of Finance lost no time in seeking to dispose of this somewhat dubious holding, for by 12th January they were already seeking report from W. Bowen Jones of Caernarfon with a view to sale. The report, when it was submitted in the October was not encouraging, Jones referred to the fact that the Abercwmeiddaw Slate Company had failed in 1907 and classed it as "A 4th rate quarry, inferior to Aberllefenni and Braich Goch, on which £60,000 had been spent".

He described it as comprising 5 galleries and a sink waterlogged to 11 yards depth, with an "attempt" at underground chambering, which had collapsed. He said that the galleries to the east were cut off, that only the main floor was working, with 13 men but that this was not the best part and it would be costly to open new galleries. He regarded the rock quality as "poor". He valued it at £2,300 and concluded with the inference that any offer should be accepted.

Wisely a further report was sought from T.O. Williams of Aberllefenni.

He described the dip of the Vein as being 59° with the strike at 50° NE, and that there were 6 floors at 20 yard vertical interval. He mentioned the mill, as being doubled in width to 30 yards, but criticised the size of the water wheel which being of only 15-20 hp did not provide enough power for the 100 men he seemed to think required to work the quarry. Having said that he really let himself rip!

He suggested that if air compressors were used and there were 25 saw tables in operation, 220 tons of slates could be produced per 4 weeks, selling at £8 per ton net. This, he alleged, would produce an annual revenue of £21,120. Costs per 4 weeks would comprise, 100 men @ £10 each, management & selling would cost £50 and Rates & Taxes £5. Adding carriage at 3/3 (16p) per ton, would give an annual cost of £14,292, yielding a profit of £6,828. This was, of course "pie in the sky" as nothing was included for fuel (he stated the water-wheel was inadequate) timber, oils and all the many small, but in total costly items that would be required on a day-to-day basis.

Appended was a valuation, much more exhaustive than his costs list but just as optimistic. It shows that in the previous 30 years much plant had been disposed of, including the steam engines and locomotive. Also that the upper incline was now gone.

4 Large Turner Bros saw tables	@£80	£	320
2 Small Owen & Sons (Caernarfon)ditto	@£40	£	80
Shafting and pulleys for above		£	100
1 Planing machine (make unspecified)		£	100
2 Dressers	@£20	£	40
1 Saw sharpener		£	20
4 Rubbish wagons	@£7.10 (7.50)	£	30

2 Iron wagon bodies	@£2	£	4
6 Trollies	@£5	£	30
3 Turntables	@£4	£	12
1 Large jib crane		£	45
300 yards of water trough	@10,(50p)	£	150
1 Water wheel		£	100
850 yards of "Railroad" (sic)	@10/(50p)	£	225
Incline drum & building		£	120
Travelling crane in mill		£	60
Smithy tools & sundries		£	20
4 Railway wagons	@ £10	£	40
		£1496	

His valuation of the quarry buildings totalled £3,870 and "development carried out" at £14,900, giving the astonishing total of £21,466. No one was killed in the rush to buy!

In 1921 Roberts sold the lease and plant to William Parry, and Dr. Cruikshank of Bow Street, for £1,700 (which Parry borrowed). They had understood that Edwin Edmunds of Hall, Harber & Thorne had said his company were prepared to buy the quarry for £4,500 cash plus 2500 £1 ordinary shares in their firm, with a seat on their board for Dr. Cruikshank.

It is not clear if Edmunds made the offer unauthorisedly or if H.H. & T. tried to beat them down from this somewhat unrealistically priced deal. Anyway, they kept on sending anodynic replies to the increasing desperate letters from Parry and his lawyers, seeking at least a deposit. In the meantime the bank pressed for the settlement of their loan to poor old Parry. he repeatedly assured them that the sale completion was imminent and suggested that even if this deal did not go through, the Braich Goch people would buy it.

In the event neither did, and Parry who had to borrow from Roberts to get the bank off his back spent almost a decade trying to unload the idle property. Eventually, in 1932 when prospects in the industry were looking better, Samuel Mason took it off his hands and was soon employing 22 men forming the Abercwmeiddaw Slate & Slab Company Ltd in 1935. He was unable to maintain continuous work and at the outbreak of war his slender operation collapsed and he had to lay off his 12 remaining men.

Description

Initial working was as a normal open terraced hillside quarry, probably with slate being dressed in waliau on the levels, and lowered by a short self-acting incline (table type?). As work developed, and waste accumulated, buildings, including an integrated mill were erected on the waste bank where all work, including roofing slate production was carried out.

Before and during, the 1870s much work was underground, but by the mid '80s they had reverted to open working. The terraces were largely quarried away as were the machine bores on two levels. The upper incline became redundant and material was brought out on the mills level by a locomotive worked tramway. The sole use of an in-quarry steam locomotive in the area.

When workings deepened into a pit, the problems of uphaulage, rubbish disposal and pumping were solved in a radical manner, by boring a tunnel from pit bottom, which emerged at a point below the mill. A haulage incline (again table type) was built. How this was powered is debatable. Archeological evidence is that it was powered by the mill wheel, documentary evidence is that it was steam powered and the Water Balance in the 1893 Sale Particulars, suggests a third alternative. Confusingly, the sketch plan accompanying those same Particulars, shows only 2 inclines, the Main exit incline and the then disused Upper incline. The plan shows two Engine Houses at either end of the Mill, suggesting that one housed the Mill engine and the other the incline engine, both supplementing the Water Wheel.

Blocks coming out of the tunnel went up the incline to the mill, rubbish was run straight out on a shelved tramway, which crossed the public road to a new tipping area. Mill waste crossed the exit incline by a bridge and was tipped to the south of the site. Finished product went down the exit incline and over a river bridge to the Upper Corris tramway. Latterly only the upper galleries may have been worked.

Remains

In spite of landscaping the constricted nature of the site requiring high retaining walls to contain tipping is obvious.

At the quarry itself the prominent feature is the "Corris binocular" machine bored twin tunnel. The right-hand bore is only about 10 metres long, the left-hand about 80 metres, there are also similar bores higher up. Hanging rail shows they were orignally much longer. There are remnants of other similar bores at Maenofferen quarry at Blaenau Ffestiniog. They may have been machine trials rather than a serious attempt to extend underground. It is possible that they were bored by the Brunton wire-rope driven disc machine, which was reported as being "put to work in a North Wales quarry". The Brunton machine although not a success, was the inspiration for the Beaumont/English self-contained, compressed air machine, used a few years later at Dover for trial boring on the early Channel Tunnel project.

From the south-western corner of the pit a strike tunnel runs for some 120 metres to a fall. From the same point is the 250 metre drainage/access tunnel. Some slate sleepers are on the ground in that tunnel.

A farm road defines the bed of the original tramway to the mill, this passes a fine range of buildings. The largest (26m x 8.5m) has all the characteristics of a small integrated mill incorporating a lean-to splitting area. Adjoining is a windowless room (6m x 6m) with a smokestack behind, suggestive of a engine/boiler room. There is no sign in either that machinery was installed, neither has any ash been found. In the 1893 plan these are described, respectively as "Slate Store" and "Oil Store". It must be assumed that this was intended as a second mill, but never used. In the other part of the rake, a Smiths Shop, is obvious. Opposite is a lavatory served by the nearby leat, which runs from the reservoir in the cwm above.

The mills area which stood on a massive platform of waste, has been levelled and largely removed in the 1990 landscaping.

Below this mill area, adjacent to the tunnel mouth, is the pit for the 50' wheel with part of the gearing and line shaft, which was some 15 feet below mill floor level. The uphaulage incline, serving the access tunnel is alongside and it can be seen how the wheel was enlarged to provide extra power, either to cope with mill enlargment or for uphaulage. There is a structure above the wheelpit to hold the haulage drum with internal stairs to allow for maintenance. On the far side of the old, upper tramway is the base for the return sheave. There is a nice revetted platform for the rubbish tramway from the tunnel.

Above the mills area there are the 5 terraces from the earlier workings, with the second from the top producing most of the present hillside waste heaps. There are traces of the old incline down.

The massive retaining walls alongside the road, including the notable cantilevered steps, and the abutments of the rubbish bridge over the road have been lost, but the walls of the exit incline have been saved, as have another set of steps near the wheelpit.

The line of connection to the Upper Corris Tramway is obvious, the river bridge having been replaced by a footbridge.

AFON DERI SH750085 (22)

Trial, underground.
This was an attempt, possibly by Williams and Humphries of Braich Goch, in the 20s, to reach the Abercorris Narrow Vein at a low level.
Description
Little more than a trial adit.
Remains
Collapsed adit, rubbish runs, ruins of a hut. Possible incline?

CWM DYLLUAN SH732088 (6)

There is a dearth of both documentary and anecdotal evidence on this Broad Vein working.

William Jones is believed to have had a Take-Note in the mid 1850s. It was abandoned around the end of the century but is unlikely to have worked anything like continuously up to then, and may well have been closed for long periods. J.A. Williams mentions his father working there and making "pig houses" in 1894-95.

It suffered from lack of transport facilities, which had it ever been built, the projected Glyn Iago line would have solved. The incline, which probably dates from an 1880s revival, could have connected to an extension of the Upper Corris Tramway.

Description
A small working, in 2 pits, and some very limited underground, probably investigative work. A great deal of work was done there but there appears to have been little output. It is unlikely ever to have been mechanised.

It is shown on the 1901 O.S. map with buildings roofed, and three short, unconnected tramways, and not marked as disused. Curiously the magnificent incline, quite out of scale with a quarry of this size, is not shown.

Remains
The site is heavily forested. The lower shallow pit working is alongside the present forestry road and there is a rubbish run with the remains of a weighhouse. There presumably was a tramway connection to join the big incline part way down, but the later roadmaking makes this impossible to determine and the levels make it unlikely.

The upper working is inaccessible, but the very fine walls of the remote-type drumhouse of the incline down to the valley floor can be seen, but the lower parts, cut in three places by the forestry road, is much degraded.

DOLFFANOG SH729104 (4)
Work started in 1866, an attempt being made to float a company with the astonishing capital of £40,000. Certainly closed shortly afterwards.

Description
A tiny working in a valley cleft, probably only a small adit with limited chambering. Improbable that it was much more than a trial. The O.S. map of 1901 shows it as Old Level, with a further Old Level shown at 723101, but this has not been located.

Remains
Difficult to positively identify working apart from a quantity of slate waste, now levelled, the adjacent building may have been connected with the working.

GLYN IAGO (or Y Glyn) SH719072 (1)
Dating from about 1899, this is usually regarded as no more than a trial on an outcrop of the Narrow Vein. From 1900 to 1905 it was owned by the Maglona Co, who sporadically employed up to 12

men. J.A. Williams states that barracks were built and 3 Bargains were let, but no product went out.

There were clearly high hopes as a start was made on a tramway from Upper Corris.

Description

A classic small underground working, in that an excavation was made, a tunnel cut from lower down the hillside, with a rise at the end to meet the digging.

Remains

Almost totally obliterated by forestry, the original digging is open and gives down into small chambers, the adit below and any building remains have been lost.

Near the site, the tramway formation has been used for the forestry road. On the Corris side of Bwlch y Corris, the trackbed for an incline down to Upper Corris exists.

MYNYDD TŶ'N Y CEUNANT SH733084 & 730082 (5)

Tiny workings, investigating the Broad Vein, the second one at least seems to have produced.

Description

Both were underground, probably just the usual investigative digs with adits roofing up into them.

Remains

Easterly site, virtually obliterated by forestry. Westerly, an adit, and an excavation higher up, both collapsed. The dressing area obliterated by forestry road. Trimming waste confirms that some product was made.

PEN Y GARREG SH735099 (9)

A re-working of the same occurrence as Dolffanog. J.A. Williams states that some work was done here at end of 19th C. and that a re-start was made in 1920s by Pickstone of Fronfelen.

Description

Underground, a single adit into a stream cleft.

Remains

Collapsed adit and waste made into a flat platform with vestiges of a small building. Some possible trimming waste, but it is far from obvious by what route the product could have been taken away.

TAP DU SH735092 (8)

Also referred to as Rugog Quarry.

A Take Note was issued to James Jenkins by Samuel Williams in 1874 to work a slate vein on Rugog farm for a rent of £30 for the first year and £50 for the second year. This does not appear to have been renewed.

Description

A small trial.

Remains

Some excavation and waste.

TŶ'N Y BERTH SH738087 (10)

In 1848 G.W. Hills of Talyllyn United Slate Quarries took a 99 year lease, at £40 pa without royalty, but the site was almost certainly worked before that. The Tŷ'n y Berth Slate Quarry Company started extensive work in 1852, and by June the shareholders were told that "100% profits were being made on raising" and that due to the diligence of Mr Joseph, the "Purser" there remained a credit balance of over £5,000. By the end of the year there were reports that work had stopped to get the bottom tunnel driven, that roofing-up had commenced to the pit and that roofing for 3 had commenced. Roofing was said to be continuing on 4, at 5 a tunnel had been commenced and a 6th was proposed. H. Hughes & Co were employed in "taking cover" for another "depth" to raise stone for the "Engine House". (translation from the Welsh "Tŷ Injan" which can be applied to any building containing machinery e.g. a water-powered mill).

By 1853, "6 tunnels with roofing to pits" were completed as were 6 cottages (2 more planned), magazine, smithy, incline, tramway, reservoir to feed the 30' x 4'8" wheel and engine house with a capacity of 10 machines. A "traverser" and 2 saws (sandsaws?) and a planer having been installed, there were 2 more planers on order. With this expenditure, plus wages of £1500 and sundries of £302 against sales of just £250, the £5000 had gone and there was a £2500 cash call. There was a further cash call the next year, and by 1858 the lease was back with Hills who traded as the Tŷ'n y Berth Slate company.

It was listed in a Slate Directory of 1858, but not afterwards, although John Parry was still "Quarry Agent" in 1861. There was a closure certainly from 1867—1875 as, according to J.A. Williams, the carpenter's workshop was leased to a Wesleyan congregation during this time. A lease of 1875 of a number of farms, including Tŷn y Berth, from A.J.S. Corbet to John Hughes Jones included a provision of slate royalties of 1/6th, although it is unlikely that much, if any extraction occurred.

The Gaewern Slate Quarry Company was floated in 1877, with the intention of taking over both that quarry and Tŷ'n y Berth. This company may not have worked this quarry, and in 1879 the even more ambitious Tŷ'n y Berth & Corris Valley Slate Company was formed with a capital of £50,000, J.G. Nolan being appointed manager. It is unlikely they did any work and were struck off in 1887.

In the 1890s it was bought by the Towyn company (afterwards Maglona), who did some small scale work. Closed by 1897.

"HILLSBOROUGH" This is a "phantom" quarry. There were at least three highly questionable company promotions. The Great Welsh Union Slate Co (1857), the Union Slate Co (1859) & the British Slate C (1860), all unsuccessfully purported to be taking over groups of quarries which included Hillsborough.

On the main road, adjacent, a row of cottages are named Hillsborough, suggesting that it was Tŷ'n y Berth they had designs on. It was not unknown for company promotions to be for quarries for which the promoters had no title, but which they hoped to buy if the flotation was successful.

Description

A series of 6 adits in tandem, following the Narrow Vein, leading to excavations out to bank, with an incline and rubbish runs. Roofing slate was cut and dressed adjacent to the adits. There was a water-powered mill and other buildings close to the main road, but no connection to the Upper Corris tramway.

J.A. Williams describes the working as being typical of the Narrow Vein quarries viz — "break the cover" i.e. excavate to prove the rock, then 25 yards lower downslope drive an adit and "roof" up to reach the excavation. He describes this roofing as "awful work" as there was little clean air to clear the dust and smoke from firing.

Remains

In forestry, comprises a series of collapsed adits and associated rubbish runs and ruins of dressing sheds. Traces of a reservoir and of the incline formation are discernable.

Near the road, the mill has been converted into a row of houses (New Street). The garage of the endmost house was the site of the water wheel. A nearby office building has an interestingly patterned slate roof.

TŶ'N Y CEUNANT SH744088 (12)

In 1836 G.H. Baker appears to have been occupier. But in 1848, Margaret Owen, Hugh Owen and David Davies, were negotiating to let it to John Hall Holdsworth and Robert M. Caley on a 21 year lease, including the houses, sheds and warehouses for £17.10 (£17.50) pa. They used, but did not register, the style Tŷ'n y Ceunant Company.

In 1849 following reports of increased output, 400 shares were offered on the "Cost book" principle. In 1851, with reports of "Full work", shares were again on offer backed by a recommendation by St Pierre Foley that investment would "Pay 100% and no Royalties were payable. Foley pointed out that "Mr Rowlands quarry" on which "£35,000 had been laid down was now "worked out". (Gaewern!?)

Anyway, in 1852 Edward Docker and George Knight Huxley took a lease on two cottages, a building "formerly a chapel" and rights to dig for 39 years from 1851 for a rent of £50. In 1855 after sale negotiations with William S. Vardy of London fell through, J.C. Morris of Fron Felen, bought the lease from Docker and Huxley. The plant being valued at £500.

In 1863 the Cader Idris Slate and Slab Quarry Co Ltd was formed with the intention of taking over the quarry from the then owner, John G. Lumby and seem to have run it for about 3 years. In 1867 the Tŷ'n y Ceunant Slate & Slab Quarry Company was formed, but they failed to make returns after 1869.

J.A. Williams says working ceased in 1878, and that the last owner was David Owen. He also states that the mill building was used as an Independent chapel. A sale of land at Tŷ'n y Ceunant in 1877 mentions a building formerly used as a chapel, suggesting that work ceased well before that.

In 1880 it was described as "idle many years". The mill

building, or one adjacent to it may have subsequently been used for processing, possibly enamelling.

Description

Pit/underground, on the Narrow Vein 2 workings with an incline down to a mill at the main road, on the far side of which were the working buildings. Oddly, there never seems to have been a connection to the Upper Corris tramway.

Remains

Little to be seen on the site itself, two pit workings with (collapsed) adits, near which are vestiges of dressing sheds etc. There is an incline formation from the adit level, down to the road.

At road level, there are cottages possibly associated with the quarry, and the walls of the mill (chapel?) still stand on the far side of the river. Lack of mill waste confirm that little slate was produced.

TŶ'N Y LLECHWEDD SH738097? (11)

Some possible early trials here.

Description

Unknown.

Remains

Forested.

The Mill at Aberllefenni c1960,
National Library of Wales.

Enamelling at Braich Goch c1960,
National Library of Wales.

The Braich Goch Mill and Offices c1950,
By kind permission of H. Townley Esq.

The 5 Level Bridge, Braich Goch c1970,
Author's collection.

Water Balance at Aberllefenni c1950,
By kind permission of H. Townley Esq.

The 4 - 6 Incline, Braich Goch c1970,
Author's collection.

The Gaewern Tramway Incline, Braich Goch, c1970,
Author's collection.

The Abercwmeiddaw Steps c1980,
Author's collection.

The Abercwmeiddaw "Binocular",
Author's collection.

The "Middle" Mill Ratgoed,
Author's collection.

"Blue Cottages" Aberllefenni,
Author's collection.

A Drumhouse at Gaewern,
Author's collection.

Foel Grochan Water Balance,
Author's collection.

Ceunant Ddu and Hen Chwarel,
Author's collection.

Ratgoed Powder House Ventilator,
Author's collection.

"Store" (Projected Mill?) and Smithy Abercwmeiddaw,
Author's collection.

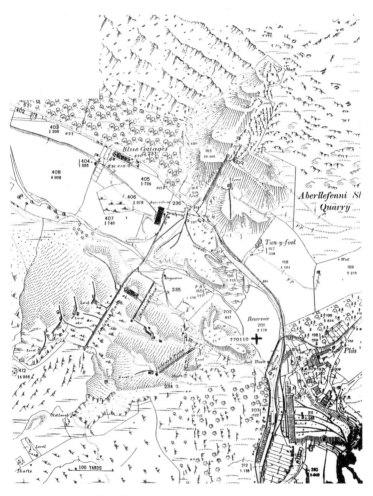

The Aberllefenni Slate Quarries, 1st O.S.
By kind permission National Library of Wales.

Section 5 ABERLLEFENNI

This is the oldest, at times the largest, and now, the sole surviving Slate operation in the Corris area. It is the only quarry in Wales that can claim almost 5 Centuries of virtually continuous operation, keeping going through wars and depressions that brought interruptions to almost all others. Its history is entirely devoid of scandals and speculations, and its rock, having been subject to similar secondary geological action as Braich Goch, is of exceptional quality.

There is some confusion as the name Aberllefenni is often applied to the quarry in the Eastern side only, which is, correctly, Foel Grochan, which together with Ceunant Ddu and Hen Gloddfa, on the Western side, make up the Aberllefenni undertaking.

The whole property has been, and still is, under common ownership so it is not usually possible to distinguish documentarily between the three sites. The same narrow Vein was worked on the two sides of the valley, which for centuries was the only point in the district where good rock outcropped close to a road.

FOEL GROCHAN SH768103 (44) CEUNANT DDU SH766099 (42)
HEN GLODDFA SH765101 (39)

A start date as early as the 14th C. has been ascribed, and it is almost certain that it was operating in 1500 when Plas Aberllefenni was apparently roofed with immediately local material. In the 17th C. the Lloyds were the landowners. In 1725 the property passed, via Ann Pryce widowed daughter of Sir John Lloyd and her daughter Mary, to the Campbells (Earls of Mansfield family). In 1801 the Hoares (the bankers) took over an interest and in 1806 the whole property passed to John Davies, (possibly a relative of the Campbells who, when he died in 1827, his will mentioned land including slate quarries "lately in the possession of Robert Jones, now Jane Evans and Robert Evans". It is probable that it was Jones who commenced vigorous work here, with 1810 as a likely starting date. There is record of 3 quarrymen employed in 1824 at a wage of 15/ (75p) per week.

Ownership passed to Pryce Jones, executor (and son-in-law?) of John Davies. In 1852 there was an offer for sale at £9,000 of at least, part of the estate, and the whole was offered in 1859.

Sale Particulars refer, inter alia, to "All those mines and quarries of first-rate slate in and under same, with the several newly erected saw-mills & workshops, nearly 40 capital cottages for workpeople, manager's house, machine house & other erections thereon, together with all and sundry plant and machinery thereto belonging, the whole of which have been obtained from the best makers, and of the latest improved descriptions, regardless of expense, and include sawing and planing machines of considerable dimensions, water-wheels of great power, weighing machines, tramroads, breaks (?), wagons, chairs, etc."

"The Aberllefenni Slate is of deep blue, possessed of considerable tenacity and hardness, but yet easily worked. It is much sought after for roofing important buildings as well as for pavements, cisterns, chimney-pieces etc. A new tramway is being constructed (Under Act of Parliament) from these Works to the river Dovey, which will tend greatly to increase the traffic, and it is also proposed to unite it at the station with the proposed railway from Newtown to Machynlleth, thus enabling the proprietors of these quarries to compete with those of Caernarvonshire for the inland traffic as well as by sea".

The outcome of the sale is not clear, but ownership of the quarry and, at least, much of the estate passed to Col. Robert Davies Jones of Trefri, Aberdyfi (a relative of John Davies?). He later adopted the name Pryce. He traded as Aberllefenni Slate Quarries. He certainly came in at the right time, for not only was rail access becoming available, but nearly two decades of prosperity for the industry lay ahead.

One of his first actions seems to have been the commissioning of their own steamship, the 83′ long "Aberllefenni Quarry Maid". It was locally built, but the engine was fitted by De Wintons at their Caernarfon works, possibly the first marine engine that firm ever installed. This bold action presaged Pryces' vigorous enterprise which developed this quarry into the most consistently successful in the area.

During the period around 1870 Robert Hughes was the energetic manager, later being succeeded by D. Jones. In 1879 their 169 men (81 underground) raised 4694 tons, but the following year it was down to 4441 tons, with some men laid off. But in 1881 in spite of dull trade generally they took men on and the next year were up to 175 men producing 4656 tons and in 1883 this increased to 4814 tons with only 2 more men on their books. These annual tonnages then declined somewhat with their manpower hovering around 150 for the rest of the decade.

1890 under the new manager, E.Ll. Evans, was a good year and their manpower reached almost 190, but by the time ownership passed to Athelstone R. Pryce (son of R.D.?) in 1891, business had taken a downturn, manpower was slashed to under 120 and there was a brief strike, but the next year the Corris Railway was commenting on the increased tonnages they were dispatching and by 1893 the tonnage was back up to 4044 with 73 men underground and 59 on the surface, and two years later the tonnage was up to 5185 with only about 140 men, giving a tonnage per man/year of 37, very high by Coris standards.

In 1897 Pryce obtained a lease from Mrs Eleanor Anwyl, to construct a dam and pipeline to abstract water to make use of the by now disused Cambergi reservoir to power an air compressor.

By 1903 M. Roberts was manager and the style Aberllefenni Slate & Slab Company was being used, and although the workforce was down to around 120, for the first time in many decades it exceeded that of Braich Goch.

In 1906 there was a curious episode, Corris Railway, always ready to level counter-allegations against the ever complaining quarries, stated that an employee William Hughes, was selling coal "on the side", taking advantage of the favourable rates on return loads of coal. There was a veiled hint that it was the quarry's coal that he was selling! Pryce stoutly defended Hughes who appears to have continued to have coal for his private and legitimate business hauled up from Machynlleth at quarry rates.

However business was still declining and in 1908 the workforce fell below 100. 1910 was a bad year, ending with only 70 employed, but by the time D. Owen took over as manager in 1912, 100 were again on the books. It was he who first bore the brunt of the wartime difficulties, and by 1916 manpower was down to under 50. Having lost their export markets, U.K. building being at a low ebb and, from 1917 on, slate workers being subject to conscription, the whole industry reached a nadir, but again Aberllefenni fared better than most.

In the short-lived boom years around 1920, the men understandably wanted "a piece of the action" and much acrimony resulted. The owners and agents seeking to present a united front, whilst the Union sought to divide them.

One must have some sympathy with the men —

There had been over the couple of decades prior to WW1 some increase in prices. For instance, Slab which had been fetching £4.00 per ton in 1890 had risen to £4.7.6 (£4.375) by 1913 (although Common Flagging remained at £1.12.6 (£1.625). Similarly First quality 24 x 14 Slates rose from £14.5.0 (£14.25) per 1200 to £15.15.0 (£15.75), over the same period. Although the prices of lower quality roofing slate had gone up rather more, there had, apart from the brief boom of 1903/04, been little scope for even the most benevolent management granting much in the way of higher wages.

However by 1921 the same Slab was fetching £17.10.0 (£17.50) and even humble flagging was making £5.00. Although roofing slate had fallen back somewhat from the 1920s peak, Firsts, 24 x 14s were still fetching £43.00, and even the humble Thirds commanded £30, against the pre-war £8.00.

The workforce saw selling prices up to 4 times and more, on pre-war levels but wages barely doubled, and rises apparently being readily granted to men in the big quarries of Blaenau and Caernarfonshire.

Management on the other hand, were faced with increased costs, two or three times pre-war prices being asked for most quarry consumables, and the traditional pool of second-hand machinery at knock down prices had gone as war-time scrap. They had no wish to return to the pre-war situation where revenues barely, if at all, covered outgoings, and they may well have realised, correctly, that these inflated prices would not last.

Some wage increases had been granted in 1919, Rockmen were getting around 6/6 (32p) per day, scarcely above the 6/3 (31p) of labourers in the large Blaenau quarries and well short of the 7/- (35p) skilled men were getting there. By 1920 the Union was citing the "going rate" as 9/3 (46p) per day for Quarrymen and Rockmen, 8/6 (42.5p) for Labourers & up to 10/3 (51p) for Carpenters and

Smiths. Aberllefenni, cautiously unwilling to allow increased basic rates that might not be sustainable granted an increase in bonuses and various concessions, such as a 30/- (£1.50) advance to newcomers. But later in the year had to concede some rises in basic rates, and made an attempt to establish a "sliding scale" e.g. 6d per day variation for every 10% increase or decrease in slate prices. The vexed question of differentials between the various categories continuing to exacerbate negotiations.

Wages edged up further in 1921, (up to over 12/- (60p) in some northern quarries), but already the price bonanza was fading, dropping 10% in 1921 and another 10% in 1922. A standard scale was granted by some of the big quarries, — Quarrymen, Letting Standard 9/10 (49p) Daily rate 8/1 (40p) with a minimum of 6/- (30p), labourers rates being 8/1 (40p), 7/4 (37p) & 5/6 (27p). The less affluent quarries felt they could not face these minima, conflict was inevitable, and in the Summer of 1922 virtually the whole of the industry came out on strike. Here, unlike some quarries, it was quickly settled and the further fall of prices in 1923 scuttled any hope the men may have had of better remuneration.

Prices and wages remained fairly constant for the rest of the 1920s as did employment here at around 100. But by the early thirties prices of roofing slate fell, in some cases by up to a quarter, and wages, particularly of the skilled men suffered, as did numbers in work. This being mainly a Slab quarry was less affected than some and they were able to keep nearly 80 men in work.

In 1932 the Official rate was Quarrymen 9/1 (45p), 8/1 (40p) & 7/3 (36p). Labourers 8/4 (42p), 7/4 (36p) & 6/8 (33p), for Letting Standard, Daily Rate and Minimum respectively. But lower bonuses meant that actual earnings went down and anyway not all quarries could afford to pay official scales. 1933 was a bad year and a 3 day week was worked for a time.

In 1935 Sir Haydn Jones M.P. (of Abergynolwyn quarry) bought Pryce out putting in T.O. Williams (who had been involved with Braich Goch), as manager and employment exceeded 100 once more.

By 1938 it was recognised that the best roofing product was inferior to that coming from further north so Firsts or Bests were no longer listed. The top quality was described as mediums, selling at £37.12.6 (£37.625), Strong Mediums were £35.10.0 (£35.50) and Seconds £32.10.0 (£32.50). They were now also listing Damp Course slate in sizes 20 x 9 at £11.7.6. (£11.37) down to 9 x 4½ at £1.10.0 (£1.50)

Slab generally was at 1921 price levels, but although a Price Card shows Flagging @ 70/ (£3.50) it is overwritten in ink as 50/ (£2.50), half of the 1921 price, reflecting the difficulty of obtaining even modest list prices.

A roofing Stock List for 1938 shows 24 listed sizes in stock mostly in all the three qualities — 57 items in all totalling over 415,000 pieces. Only about a sixth were in the popular 24 x 12 sizes, over half were the rarely demanded 10 x 8s & 10 x 6s, with many of the other sizes in trifling quantities. The number of items and the probability that half the value of stock was in very slow movers illustrates the difficulties of stock keeping in an industry where the variety you produce is largely dictated by the occurrence of the rock rather than by current customer demand. These slates would mainly have come from the western side quarries, where, in the 1990s slates possibly forming part of this very stock list remained isolated at the top of Hen Gloddfa.

The war again brought difficulties, the immediate pre-war total of over 120 men dropped to 40 in 1944.

The immediate post-war era, to an extent followed the same pattern as that of a generation before. Wage rates in all quarries had failed to match those of industry in general and in 1947 there was a strike. Many of the then 70 workforce found temporary employment building a forestry road to Aberangell, and though the present road follows a slightly different route the massive abutments for a Bailey bridge they constructed remain at SH792108. The problem was that Braich Goch had followed the North Wales Quarry Association in awarding 11d (4.5p) per day extra for Quarrymen and 10d (4p) for Labourers. Sir Haydn Jones and T.O. Williams refused to pay saying that the low rent of the company cottages more than compensated for the difference. Arbitration eventually awarded the men 5d (2p) & 4d (1.7p) respectively, and following an ultimatum, work re-started, but with a reduced workforce.

In fact management were fortunate that when the dispute was settled so many of the men came back. Earlier that year when the Cambrian quarry at Glyn Ceiriog suspended work due to exceptionally bad weather, the men were taken on by the local Council to assist with snow-clearance. Having experienced easier work and higher wages, so few men opted to return to that quarry that it never reopened.

A petty cash book confirms that in the late 1940s acetylene lamps were used, carbide being purchased in bulk, although some electric lamps (240v) were bought. In 1950 they bought Abergynolwyn's stock of candles (432lb) which at that time were still being sold to the men for illumination underground. Curiously hacksaw blades were bought in large quantities.

During the 1950s only some 40 were employed, all work being at Foel Grochan, under the managership of J.A. Williams.

In 1956 Mr Dewi F. Lloyd and his brother Mr Gwilym Lloyd, took over, trading as Wincilate Ltd (whose present directors are Mr John Lloyd [Dewi's son] and Mr Walter Simonds). The Lloyds vigorously modernised the mill and rationalised the underground work. They faced something of a task as the quarry had been worked with more thought for immediate profit than long term prospects. Much waste had been backfilled effectively sterilising chambers which still have large amounts of unworked rock. The make to waste ratio had been an incredible 1-67. They immediately took steps to reduce this prodigality, and further improved the ratio by extracting rock by the use of a Korfmann chainsaw (which had just been developed for the moving of the Abu Simbel tomb in Upper Egypt during the construction of the Aswan high dam). Later, wiresawing supplemented the chainsaw and make to waste ratio now runs at 1-3, undoubtedly an industry record. The company, in 1991, won a Rural Enterprise award for their contribution to the rural economy.

Regrettably numbers employed have decreased to a dozen or so, reflecting modernisation, rather than falling output.

Description, Foel Grochan SH768103

The Vein dips at 70deg to the southeast and runs almost continuously right through the Foel Grochan mountain. The rock is dense, does not split readily and lacks "jointing" so the product has always been predominately Slab, albeit of exceptional quality.

Early working was in a big cavern high on the hillside, later called "Alma", from where in 1853 it was reported that a 125 ton, (17' x 10' x 9'10"), block was taken.

Later work was entirely underground, the methodology being bold and unusual, contrasting with the usual Meirionnydd practice of upward working, the working here was basically downward. So unusual was it that in 1882 C.Le N. Foster, (later Sir Charles), H.M. Inspector of Mines produced a paper describing it.

Tunnels were bored along the strike (i.e. at right angles to the dip), through the "hard", immediately under the slate, that is, on the northern side of the vein. There were 8 tunnels in all, at vertical intervals of about 60 feet, the lowest being at valley floor level. Work commenced by roofing up chambers, from the highest tunnel, until bad rock was encountered or a breakthrough to bank was made, leaving a flat floor in the slate at tunnel level. The chambers being 100' to 187' long with 24'-30' of rock left, between them to provide supporting pillars.

Then, from the floor which had been created, a vertical shaft was made down from each chamber to the tunnel below, and by working outward and downward from this shaft, the chamber floor was cut away. Both blocks and rubbish being lowered down the shaft to the lower tunnel by a winch in the upper tunnel, via a rope reeved through a pulley in the roof. Trucks of material were then trammed away along the lower tunnel to the adit, good block going down the incline and rubbish tipped. As work progressed downwards men reached the working area by descending chain ladders.

When the level of the lower tunnel was reached, a fresh shaft was sunk to the next tunnel below and the process repeated until the lowest tunnel was reached.

An incline originally served almost the topmost levels, but as working progressed it was shortened as the lower levels were brought into use. Five drumhouses being successively used.

Subsequent working was, and still is, downwards below lowest adit level. Most of the upper tunnels ran right through the mountain and in the 1950s some material was removed "through the back door", a crane being used to facilitate this. Blocks were taken to the mill by tractor-pulled trailer.

Rubbish disposal was a problem, much was tipped from the front adits, a little was trammed out of the adits on the eastern side, but some was "back-filled" in abandoned chambers. Any waste from the lowest adit or which came down the incline, and waste from the original mill, had to be tipped on the valley floor. To gain height to enable this to be done, two water balanced inclines were employed to reach the top of the waste banks.

The original mill was opposite the foot of the incline but in the 1860s a large mill was built at Aberllefenni village, near the terminus of the Corris Railway. This was served by a big new reservoir.

The Aberllefenni tramway which connected the quarry with the mill, remained in use until the 1970s, (although latterly tractor powered). It was thus the last survivor of the quarry tramways. Prosaically, a fork-lift truck is now used.

Remains, Foel Grochan
Viewed from a distance the prominent feature is the "Alma" cavern which extends from level 4 up to level 3. Adits 1 & 2 are not obvious, a great deal of waste has been tipped down the mountainside from these four uppermost levels. Waste from 5,6 & 7 has been trammed out on conventional rubbish runs. There are several structures on the valley floor, some ruined, some still in use. The main items of interest are the water balances, one near the 8 adit and one at the far side of the valley. Both are relatively complete, particularly the more distant one which has almost all pipework in situ (and, curiously, chains for holding down the drum).

The big incline, in its final truncated form from Level 7, is still in fair condition. It was converted from a conventional balanced table incline into a single-action, the counterbalance being provided by a rubble filled box.

Near the adit are the modern compressor house, the workshop hut and an old building that was, until the 1980s, the office. The old, water powered compressor house exists and alongside are traces of the original mill, its leat and sluice (near Blue Cottages) being traceable. So is the pipe for the compressor turbines, which re-used the old Cambergi reservoir. Its dam rebuilt with a fine brick-stepped spillway. There are two penstock towers, accessed by bridges partly made of bridge rail, one controlled the drain, the other the feed-pipe. On the road to the mill some rail of the old tramway is still in place.

At SH 773106 the workings were accessed from the east, there is a Rushton crane (Yr hen Grein Goch) which in the 1950s was used to raise material from the back chambers. At a higher level is part of an old hand-winch which earlier served the same purpose. There is a trackway which was used to haul blocks round the hill by tractor to the mill.

Underground, the working down from the highest level has produced a number of spectacular chambers, most breaking out to bank.

There are theoretically 13 chambers, but bad rock and some haphazard working breaks the strict continuity.

1 Adit is at 1010' a.s.l. (at western end) with some chambering up, 2 at 960', 3 at 890', 4 at 840', 5 at 680', 6 at 590', 7 at 460' & 8 at 400' (Valley floor level).

Below the 8 original adit levels, there was a slant, now abandoned and flooded going down to Drift level at about 350' a.s.l. and old workings in chamber 5, extend over 100' below this. Thus the total vertical extent is around 800'.

In the 1980s working was concentrated in chamber 3, sinking down below Level 8. Blocks are lifted to that level by a crane and taken out to the adit entrance by a battery-electric loco. It is of interest that in spite of the radical changes that have been made in methods of extraction and reduction, the workings are still reached by the traditional chain-ladders.

The more easterly chambers do not extend down to Level 8 and were reached by the 7 tunnel which runs from near the head of the truncated incline, which was abandoned in the 1960s.

On the eastern side near the Rushton crane a tunnel runs in to gallery above some chambers where there is a power-winch, (a steam winch compressed-air operated), which handles material as described by Sir Charles Foster.

The reservoir to power the mill at the village, is a nice feature with its slate leats and sluices (it still provides water for cooling and washing). The dam is traversed by the trackbed of the Ratgoed tramway. There is a fine chapel-like building with a bell, that used to be the office.

The mill, which once had 20 saw-tables, has been re-equipped with modern machines, including several large diamond saws. There are also polishing and edging machines, some of which were brought from Caernarfon, when the company's works at Victoria dock closed in 1988. Outside in its own building is a large horizontal, multiple frame saw, (unique to the industry). Unfortunately, the mill water wheel has long since gone.

Although something of a disappointment to the Industrial Archaeologist, the mill is probably the best equipped in the industry. Some finishing work is carried out at their "Inigo Jones" works at Groeslon, Caernarfon.

The network of track outside the mill was lifted in the 1980s. Some older machines and notable old lifting equipment is still in place, or to be found lying about. There are, in the village some interesting dwellings, many of them built by the quarry company, forming a very much "one industry" community. The present company office used to be the Post Office.

An electricity plant, from 1920s, on the Nant Llwydiarth, once supplied the quarry and village. Some traces remain.

Description, Ceunant Ddu

Underground, with some early open working.

On a spur of the Narrow Vein, geological disturbance having caused the Vein to overlap producing two occurrences partially separated by the unwanted "Red Vein". This working is virtually contiguous with Hen Gloddfa, on the main Vein, which continues across the valley to Foel Grochan. The names Ceunant Ddu and Hen Gloddfa (or Hen Chwarel) are used interchangably for the whole western side.

The slate is somewhat different from that obtained on the eastern side, being less dense, duller in colour, but it does readily split to produce good roofing material.

It is likely that the earliest extraction took place here. Much working was open, but as with all Narrow vein quarries, it was mainly underground, being worked on 6 levels in much the same manner as Foel Grochan, but on a much more limited scale. An incline system brought material down to the mill, which was originally on the hillside, at level 4, such a building being shown, roofed, on 1901 O.S. Later when extraction was being carried out at lower levels, blocks were trammed across the valley.

Slate making was done up on the levels, R. Hughes, the innovative manager of the 1870s is reputed to have developed a treadle operated trimmer for use on this site with the intention of enabling mechanical trimming to be done on the levels, rather than in the mill. It may have been he who was responsible for the experiments with mechanical splitting reputed to have been done here.

Remains, Ceunant Ddu

The site is much degraded, at the top levels (1 & 2) there are some chamberings out to bank which may more properly be considered part of Hen Gloddfa. There are faint traces of possible inclines at these higher levels.

On level 3 there is the eroded trace of a connection with Hen Gloddfa, on Level 5 there are remains of dressing sheds and the most notable feature of the site — the drumhouse at the head of the degraded incline down to 6, has a drum made almost entirely of wood, a fine example of the wheelwright's art. At Level 6, is another adit, nicely portalled, with some concrete bases adjacent, more buildings and close by the abovementioned water balance.

The original route whereby material was carted out along the valley is obvious. There is anecdotal evidence that this was railed but there are no documentary or archaeological grounds to support this.

Description, Hen Gloddfa

An arm of the Narrow Vein was worked, some early working was open but most development was underground. The underground methodology was not unlike Foel Grochan quarry, with 7 adits No. 1 at 1010' asl, 2 at 960', 3 at 890', 4 at 840', 5 at 680', 6 at 470', & 7 at 380', with a slant going below 7 to workings down to about 320' asl. These lowest workings were in use until the mid 1960s. Development extended to 6 chambers.

Again unlike Foel Grochan the slate here splits readily, giving a good roofing product although not as thin as say, Blaenau material. Slate making was, as at Ceunant Ddu, carried out up on the levels in Waliau.

The bad rock which divides the narrow vein at this point pinches out back from the summit so that the workings are not really distinguishable from Ceunant Ddu.

There was a water powered mill on Level 4. The 1889 O.S. shows an incline, straight down past the mill down to the valley floor and across the valley to the old Foel Grochan mills area and the head of the Aberllefenni tramway. There was a late intention to make a new incline from the highest level, but this was never completed.

Remains, Hen Gloddfa

At the highest level is a dressing floor still with a stock of slate, also some rail & trucks. A massive dry stone construction suggest that a ropeway was used as a pro-tem arrangement pending completion of an incline. There is a partly built drumhouse and table incline and the complete kit of Cast Iron parts (Unused) for the making of a drum (Axle, Brakedrum [6' Dia.], 2 Spiders & 1 Brake Spider [5' Dia.]) and the Coalbrookdale Co winch used to raise these heavy components. There is a modern shaft which was a 1970s investigation into untopping. A fine road was built to access this so far abortive exercise.

Immediately below, on Level 1, there are old open workings and a reservoir. Level 2 is largely lost in subsequent open operations, but there are traces of a vertical shaft. An adit and a leat system including some fine slate troughing 18" wide by 4" deep made of ¾" thick slabs jointed together with ends rebated and sealed and reinforced by iron rod.

There is a tramroad connection running to a remote type drumhouse, set well back with extended brake control. This level 3 which is the lower limit of open quarrying, has an embanked tramroad towards the south, to the head of a table incline, which was possibly never completed. There are some vestiges of buildings. On Level 4 at the bottom of the table incline, an embanked track runs south to a curious drumhouse built into and truncating a steep incline down from Level 2. This tiny remote-type drumhouse with a banksman's cabin alongside, has a brake adapted to suit the unusual juxtaposition. There is an adit, open, with rails in situ at this level and some building remains, undoubtedly the old main mill as there is a rubbish run for mill waste running south from it and also to the south another short incline (for finished product?).

Level 5, has the ruins of some dressing sheds, and the formation of a connection to the above mentioned incline with the curious drumhouse, which comes down from 4. Level 6 is built up on waste originating from its adit and also waste up-hauled on the adjacent water balance. Adit 7 is at valley floor level almost overwhelmed by waste. This adit, which, unusually is a downward drift, was reopened during an underground investigation in the late 1980s.

Underground, there is some chambering at various levels.

As a working, subject to mines regulations, tresspass can bring prosecution.

However the management will treat sympathetically serious applications to view the surface structures.

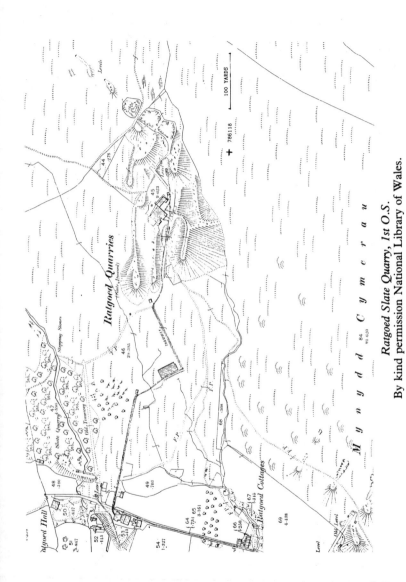

Ratgoed Slate Quarry, 1st O.S.
By kind permission National Library of Wales.

Section 6 THE RATGOED VALLEY

This valley, properly Cwm Ceiswyr, is so identified with the Ratgoed quarry and its eponymous tramway, that this anglicised form of R'alltgoed has become its adopted name. Appropriately, as for almost a century the quarry dominated the valley, and for much of that time the tramway was its only thoroughfare. Oddly, for though the Ratgoed quarry was so well known and had quite extensive surface structures it was in fact quite small and for a number of years the less regarded Cymerau quarry was in fact larger. Of the other two quarries, Dolgoed produced little and Ffynnon Badarn was only a trial.

CYMERAU SH779116, 777111 & 777106 (46)

A lease of 1863 to H.N. Hughes probably marks the start of working here. An offshoot of Ratgoed, for most of its life under the same ownership and managment. By 1876 its owners were recorded as "Hughes & Nephew" with G.F. Griffiths as manager. An A.W. Chalmers was shown as trustee for Hughes and Nephew in 1879, with 33 men producing 559 tons under D. Owen, the Ratgoed manager. J. Rowlands seems to have had an interest as that year he made over at least part of his own holding to H.N. Hughes.

In 1880 tonnage was up to 709 with 36 men, (13 underground). By 1881, they were trading as Ratgoed & Cymerau Slate quarries, Evan Griffiths being manager of both, holding office until almost the end of the century.

1882 saw 688 tons produced by 29 men improving to 762 tons the following year with the same number of men, a great increase in productivity but still only marginally economic. Manpower hovered around 25 for the rest of the decade but by 1891 was down to a mere 18. The Meirionedd Mines Enquiry of 1893/4 lists them as having 11 men underground and 10 men on the surface producing 530 tons.

In 1898 the executors of the late H.N. Hughes having failed the previous year to sell to the abortive Ratgoed Slate & Slab Quarries venture, the new Ratgoed manager, Daniel Davies saw his payroll here of 11, decline to 4, then to nil in 1900. Along with Ratgoed it was bought by W.J. Lewis, but for the next two decades it existed virtually in limbo as an outstation of Ratgoed.

In 1921, the 1863 lease now held by Mr & Mrs Lewis of Ratgoed Hall, was taken over by Inigo Jones of the Tudor Slate Works, Groeslon, Caernarfon. who, pre-war had worked Robell quarry (SH784233). They put 8 men to work. The agreement allowed Lewis to have the use of the mill for 6 months with a guarantee of water supplies for the turbine, presumably so that he could finish off work on blocks in hand. The trading style of Cymerau Slate Quarries was used.

Ownership later passed to Jones' nephew Kennedy Jones and then his son Harry Jones. They sawed and planed here, finishing and enamelling being done at Groeslon works, (now owned by the Wincilate company). They were still trading as Cymerau Slate Quarries in 1933, but with only 5 employed, 2 being underground. By 1936, the 5 men were registered as all working above ground. Little work was done after this. Officially abandoned in 1949.

Description

Not an easy quarry to work as the original 5 chambers, adjacent to the mill were partly below river level and had to be pumped by waterwheel, which may have been used for hauling also. R. Jones states that the Waterwheel pumped by cams, feed being by timber launder which crossed the tramway near the wheel. It was scrapped during WWII having been out of use for years. The mill was powered by a 75 h.p. Pelton wheel, fed by a pipe, electric power being brought in 1936.

The two further series of diggings higher up the valley did not have water problems, but their separation must have caused difficulties. The northernmost, close to the Ratgoed boundary, was productive with 4 chambers, and had an incline at the foot of which some sawing was done, although on this site no trace of a mill has been found nor does it appear on maps.

The other, later, intermediate adits, seem to have been less successful. These could be the "New workings" which the Corris Railway reported in 1885. They are shown on the 1891 O.S. but as disused on the 1901 edition.

Waste disposal from these workings seems to have been a problem as in 1888, they were in trouble for blocking the river causing the tramway to be flooded.

The Meirionedd Mines Enquiry shows the lowest adit at 545'
and their highest at 615' which if correct suggests that the
uppermost parts were not then in use.

Remains

At 779116 there is a series of 4 adits. The top most leads to a shaft
down, the 2nd to a sinc. The 3rd & 4th are run in. Near the upper
adits are further trials. There are traces of a drumhouse and an
incline. At valley floor are many sawn ends but no traces of a mill,
possibly there may have been an unhoused saw.

At 777111 there are several run-in adits. There are some sawn
ends suggesting a portable saw may have been used for re-working.
There are traces of a magazine, alongside the tramway, which may
have been latterly shared with Ratgoed.

At 777107 is an old adit that has been roofed up from a chamber
below. At 777106 there are, near to the bridge, ruins of the wheel
mounting and in the adjacent adit (flooded) is a remnant of the
pumping gear, (the rails which were in-situ have now gone). The
mill and other buildings are in re-use. Cottages associated with the
quarry are still in occupation. There is a surprisingly great amount
of development and mill waste.

Upstream is a reservoir, with a nice valve chamber and spillway.
The feedpipe is buried but traceable, with a surge-pit partway
along.

DOLGOED SH781126 SH7822122 SH782123 (47)

All the above are on Dolgoed property. 781126 is sometimes
assumed to be the quarrying site, but it is not apparently on
cleavable rock so it may have just supplied stone for building.

In 1848 a quarry is mentioned as being formerly in tenure of
John Owen and afterwards, Evan Owen (Decd), latter David
Evans and David Howell appear to have been interested, although
it is not certain if it was this site that was referred to.

The quarry mentioned in a Mining journal of 1869, and later
elsewhere, is undoubtedly one or both of the later two locations.
Sometimes supposed to be outliers of Ratgoed they are in fact not
on that property.

Idle by 1877, G.W. Griffiths, disillusioned with Cambergi and
getting nowhere with Hengae considered taking it over, and
commissioned a report from E. Evans, the manager of Bryneglwys
quarry (SH695054).

Evans reported that it was on the Broad Vein and that it had excellent prospects and that there was the possibility of exploiting it as three separate quarries. He pointed out that a tramway had recently been constructed to "the foot of the hill, close to the properties". He said that £10,000 would enable it to be opened and that for £20-25,000 operations on a large scale might be undertaken. He instanced that for say, £12,000 a unit with 9 Sawing-tables, 3 Planing machines and 5 Double Dressers could be started.

Replying to Griffiths' queries, Evans agreed that it was "not impossible" that the Narrow Vein might be struck, but that Broad Vein rock was proving profitable elsewhere. He emphasised that a start could not be made cheaply. Griffiths, who was clearly deterred by Evans' sums, sought advice from R. Hughes, manager of the Aberllefenni quarry. Hughes could give little comfort costwise, saying that £12-15,000 would be called for, instancing that at Abercwmeiddaw £10,000 had been spent in "not a year" and they had only 2 headings to show for it. He quoted some costs of plant — 12 Saws would be required @ £50 each, 6 Planers @ £100 each, a 40' Water Wheel would cost £150 and that shafting and pulleys would cost £100. He added that it was idle as the present partners were "of the working class, and have no money". Griffiths did not pursue it further.

The firming of prices in the late 1880s seems to have encouraged a restart. The will of John Owen who died in 1890, leaving his estate largely to Evan Jones Owen referred to "mines" for slate being worked by N.B. Owen & J.V. Owen. The quarry appears on the Inspector of Mines list for 1890. Thereafter, apart from one listing in 1894 there is no further mention.

Description

In spite of the grand plans these were scarcely more than holes in the ground.

Remains

On the northernmost site, reclamation has eliminated almost all traces. On the other two sites there clearly was some limited Slate working, one or possibly both, went underground. There are no buildings other than possible vestiges of a dressing shed.

FFYNNON BADARN SH775114 (45)

This was a late and unsuccesful underground trial. In 1890 Henry Owen of Dolgoed let a 3 year Take Note to E.H. Davies to dig for slate on Ffynnon Badarn farm at a rent of £6 for the first year, £11 for the second and £16 for the 3rd. He must have had high hopes, for in the same year, he obtained agreement from his neighbour R.D. Pryce to allow a tramway to cross Pryce's land to connect with the Ratgoed tramway near where it crosses the river at Cymerau mill.

Description

A single trial adit.

Remains

Adit and small tip on hillside.

RATGOED SH787119 (48) Also known as Allgoed (and as R'alltgoed)

Although one of the better known quarries, with a long and interesting history, it was a relatively minor working.

Horatio Nelson Hughes' 1840 will mentions the mortgaging of quarries to T. Blackburn and his intention to bequeath them to William Hughes (his nephew?) and John Rowlands, who were in partnership at that time, presumably in this enterprise, which had been started some years before. A lease between Evan Jones and William Hughes, described as a quarry agent, and John Rowlands was mentioned. Curiously, in 1844, there was an assignment of interest by William Hughes to H.N. Hughes and there was mention of him proposing to acquire John Rowlands's share, which presumably did not occur.

There seems to have been a closure in the late 1840s as a re-start is recorded in 1851 when sales ran at around £100 per month, with Slab, (including washstands, "chimneys" & headstones) and roofing slate contributing equally. Some development was taking place as William Owen was paid £23 for "making a new railway". There is also mention of clearing "The great fall" of some years previously. At the end of that year, a cargo was shipped, jointly with Aberllefenni on the "Mermaid", (At Derwenlas?).

At this time wages were being paid for "Enamelling" which included women, it being exceedingly rare for female names to appear, in any capacity in a slate quarry payroll, but they were presumably not at the quarry but elsewhere, possibly Machynlleth.

In 1853 there was an Abstract of title, from Evan Owen, Hugh Owen, John Owen, to John Rowlands, Bridget Hughes & David Howell at rent of £15, this being, one assumes, for land on neighbouring Dolgoed.

That same year the wages book shows bargains having been paid up to about £20 for a 4 week month after stoppages e.g. Candles 11/, (55p), Powder 14/ (70p), Doctor 2/ (10p). Rents for the company cottages were 12/ (60p) per month. There were many non-productive costs such as "clearing", "incline" & "rising" and the construction of the reservoirs, maintenance of which was to appear as a constantly recurring item.

By this time Rowlands had put together "Alltgoed Consols" to take over his interest in this quarry, (and also Gaewern), trading as Alltgoed Slate & Slab Quarry Company, with H. Moss as chairman.

A Company meeting in 1853 was told that over a 4 month period the balance had improved from £4612 to £4736, represented by sales of £1383 less "Costs" of £1216, "Travelling" £8 and Rent £35. (These totals would have included Gaewern). A proposal that Rowlands should buy back Ratgoed was vetoed. It was reported that reservoir construction was well ahead and that the floodgates of the main one would shortly be installed. Machinery to saw and plane would follow to give "great advantage". (A few months previously rails and "circular" tables had been ordered). This seems to infer that hand-sawing had been done up to then.

It was predicted that Ratgoed would be the equal of Moelgrochan (Foel Grochan) where it stated 2 bargains produce "70 — 100 tons per month". Shareholders were assured that they would not regret their investments. In June the 100 tons sold had realised £170, allegedly double the cost of production.

In early 1855 at a meeting of the Company, with F. Howard in the chair, Rowlands reported that sales of roofing slates were up 50% and that they could not produce enough Slab to meet orders. The £221 spent on a new incline and "slate shed" had enabled 4 men to do the work previously done by 10, so showing a saving of £15 per month. It was proposed that if a further £2000 was spent on a new engine house, saws, planers and an incline, then further expansion could take place.

But things were not going as all shareholders would wish. In April that year dissidents claimed they had got agreement to appoint Dickson of Bangor to inspect and report. Rowlands'supporters denied this, saying that in March a creditable 200 tons had been raised (this figure presumably including Gaewern). In January 1856, a letter to the Mining Journal, alleged that Rowlands had, in 1851, promised 5000 tons of output per month and that shares had been taken up on this promise. At a special meeting called with Black in the chair Rowlands was roasted. He was accused of neglect, of piling rubbish on good rock, of not allowing proper pillars and that he had allowed the late Secretary, Mr Joseph, to mis-apply funds, Howard defended him saying that the quarries were now paying, but it was agreed to form a shareholders committee.

A further meeting gave Rowlands more stick, this time for the failure of the recent share issue. Of the 20,000, £2 shares only 6000 had been taken up, although one shareholder suggested that the Crimean War accounted for the "dull times". Rowlands stated in effect that he had made no promises on output and that it was his intention to concentrate production at Gaewern, where £3000 had been spent on development. The 4th quarter of 1856 showed sales (again including Gaewern?) of only £491 with a profit of £44 and a stock grown to £1470, but with the war over confidence was expressed that matters would improve.

In 1864 the Alltgoed company having faded from sight, ownership was shown as John Rowlands and H.N. Hughes, with David Howell, John (W?) Rowlands, Bridget T. Hughes & Edward Morgan interested parties. But shortly after this H.N. Hughes seems to have bought Rowlands share of the property for £700 on behalf of Bridget Hughes. Tracing ownership is not easy as the son of John Rowlands, John W. Rowlands is sometimes referred to without his second initial and he in fact shortly pre-deceased his father.

Understandably, with the tramway fully open, 1864 was a year of some activity. In the summer, the agent (or manager) David Davies built an "Engine House", costs of £10 for masonry [160 yards @ ⅓ (6p)] plus wages of £1 6 0 (£1.30), 6½ days @ 4/- (20p) and "20 square" of timber @ 8/- (40p) being recorded. A turbine was installed by James Hayward (This was the Upper Mill?) A

"Small Incline" was also built. Various other costs are shown in the Cost book of that year — "Wheeling blocks" 1/3 (6p) per ton, another entry for the same task was 3d (1.2p), (perhaps they were not wheeled as far!)

There was also some development such as "Driving a level", cost 30/- & 33/- (£1.50 & £1.65) per yard. "Opening" cost 6/- (30p) per yard on one occasion, whilst on another it cost 5/- (25p) but with an additional daily payment of 3/- (15p) per day. "Cutting loose end" was also charged at 6/-. Rubbish clearers were paid 2/- (10p) per ton. "Clearing fall" took 22 days @ 2/6 (12.5p) per day.

The reservoir costs were recurring e.g. Puddling, 18 days @ 2/6 (12.5p) per day. This was, eventually to prove of no avail as in 1936 the larger dam broke, destroying the smaller dam.

There was also some expenditure on plant. 2 pulley blocks cost £7.10.9 (£7.54), a donkey was bought for £1.11.0 (£1.55), plus 11/9 (57p) for harness. Afterwards "Bran for donkey" was a recurring expense. An item of £2 for horseshoes equalled a month's wages for the Clerk, David Owen.

William Ellis, the Foreman was paid £5 per month, but he was later paid more, rising to a dizzy £6.9.0 (£6.45) and the dignified title of Agent. This was less than a partner in a good bargain might sometimes gross, but he did not suffer deductions for tools, powder, candles etc, and it was a regular payment. The carpenter seems to have got steady money — 3/6 (17.5p) per day, but his mate, only got 1/8 (8p).

Sales seem to have been mostly Slab. Over 3' long x 1¼" thick, fetching 72/- (£3.60) per ton, 1½" 67/- (£3.35) and 1" 78/- (£3.90). Under 3 feet long, the prices were 40/- (£2.00), 45/- (£2.25) & 50/- (£2.50), respectively. Hearthstones & sills were also sold.

Carriage cost, by tramway, was 3/6 (17.5p) per ton to Derwenlas (Quay Ward), 2/9 (14p) to Machynlleth & 1/2 (6p) to Corris. There are also payments shown of 1/3 (6.5p), 11d (4.5p), and 6d (2.5p) to Humphrey Hughes for the same destinations, but it is not clear how much each load was.

The cost book of 1866 shows separate payments to David Davies for sawing and planing, unusual, as the reduction of blocks was normally part of the "Bargain" system. Payments were made to Cymerau for smith work and the reservoir repairs again were a constant expense.

In 1868 William Ellis appears as agent, and there is mention of reservoir enlargement.

In 1873, with D. Owen, promoted from clerk to manager, a "New mill" account appears, (Middle mill?), among the costs of this was the "making of arches" @ 5/ (25p). The selling of "chimney slips" and of billiards tables was mentioned.

By 1873 roofing slate was being sold by the unusual count of a hundred e.g. 24 x 14 @ 3/9 (18.75p) per 100 & 14 x 10 @11d (4.6p), suggesting very poor stuff being sold off locally. Slab prices seem have averaged only around £2.5.0 (£2.25) per ton, even in the larger sizes.

In 1876 G.F. Smith took over as manager, with about 40 men and for a time profits continued, e.g. in September 1878 costs were £104.15.10 and sales £254.14.5, which, save some poor months, had been typical for the past decade or so, but by 1879 with prices diving, things started to go wrong, for instance in October costs were over £86 whilst sales were only £75 and by the end of year work was suspended.

H.N. Hughes took over personally, in 1881, re-started, and by the summer, monthly sales had picked up to £152 whilst costs were held at £85. In 1883 April sales were down to £93 with costs of £90 and by October sales were down to £32 with costs of £71, in the whole of the year the 25 men only managed about 400 tons, presenting the manager, Evan Griffiths with problems.

During the rest of the '80s monthly outgoings seem to have been held down to around £50, with the workforce cut back to around 15, but sales seem to have rarely covered costs, in fact in January 1886 costs were £80 and sales under £25.

That year, H.N. Hughes having died, his affairs remained in executors hands for some years, with W.R. Hughes for a time involved. This was when W.J. Lewis came into the picture, buying in through the Towyn Co. (other directors; T. Harper, E. Thomas, A.T. Carr & Peter Bennion). Griffiths remained as manager.

By the '90s there was some improvement in the company's fortunes but only by rigorous containment of outgoings, with a workforce cut to under a dozen. The Meirionedd Mines Enquiry of 1893/4 lists them as employing 7 men underground and 5 above ground producing 232 tons, somewhat up on the previous few years.

At this time there was still some good roofing trade. Hall & Rogers, Manchester taking 18 x 10 (Viscountesses?) & 20 x 10 (Countesses), whilst G.W. Wild of Wigan and Bridge of Wigan seemed also to take 24 x 12s (Duchesses). Roofing slate also sent to Smith of Wigan and Williams & Co, Newtown. As was usual nearly all output went to merchants.

Towards the end of the century they were having to move increasingly to the less profitable Slab. Griffiths & Davies, Bristol. Sessions, Cardiff. Brown & Groves, Worcester. Gee & Co, Gloucester, The Aberystwyth Enamelling Co, and the Hull Enamelling taking regular supplies. 1¼″, 1½″, 1¾″ & 2½″ being the usual thicknesses but they were having to take some Slab business at only ¼″ thickness, i.e. virtually a roofing slate, but sold at a Slab price. "Pairs of Slips", "Mantles", shelves & "Stands" were also sold, usually to more local buyers. J.A. Williams instances typical 1897 Slab prices as 57/6 (£2.87) — 70/ (£3.50), inclusive of carriage 3/1 (15p).

There were hopes in 1897, of selling out with the formation of the Ratgoed Slate & Slab Quarry Ltd, but this failed and the Towyn company was forced to increase its capital to £65,000 by the creation of 5,000 new £1 shares, H. Haslam and J.K. Andrews joining the board. The decline continued, the new manager, Daniel Davies having to cut his manpower to 8, then to nil in 1900.

Things were going wrong throughout the group (renamed Maglona Quarries Ltd in 1899) which now included Cymerau, Llwyngwern, Rhiw'r Gwreiddyn, Abercorris and by this time, Glyn Iago. Loans of £79,000 were outstanding which exceeded its borrowing powers so these were voted to be increased to £110,000 but even this was not enough as later this figure was increased to £125,000. By 1906 they ceased to trade, even their secured creditors receiving only 2/6 (12½p) in the £.

W.J. Lewis had taken over Ratgoed personally when it closed and he re-opened it 1901 with J. Jenkins as manager and 9 men, rising in 1902 to 17 making 420 tons, but although this was a boom time for roofing slate, Slab prices were weak with chimney pieces, for instance, down 15% on recent figures. In 1903 they again had to close.

A restart was made in 1907 with 27 men, exceeding 30 by 1911. R. Lumbley took over from Jenkins in 1913, but he was soon to see things hit by the war and by 1918 although then grandly styled "Ratgoed Quarries Ltd, makers of Urinals, Lavatories, Brewers and Chemicals Tanks, Cisterns, Shelving, Billiards etc", they only employed 6 men.

They like other quarries were caught up in the industrial problems of the post-war era, and the understandable demands for higher wages.

In a 1920 letter to the North Wales Quarrymens Union, W.J. Lewis dis-associated himself from any agreement made with "slatemakers" which he roundly declared they were not, with an inference that as Slab men, theirs was superior calling. But in fairness, although their basic pay seems to have been below any agreed rates, the actual totals paid in 1922, particularly for the skilled men, as much as 9/10 (49p) per day, were high for the area. Evan Lloyd was agent by this time, with 15 men under him.

In 1924 Hall Harber & Thorne Ltd (who also ran Llwyngwern) moved in, doubled the workforce, putting in their own man, E.W. Edmunds to run things. They described themselves as "suppliers of Slates, Cisterns, Electric Switchboards, Billiards Table Beds and Chimney Pieces, plain & enamelled". By 1929 E. Lloyd the Llwyngwern manager was in charge, but he employed less than 20. Shortly afterwards the Lewis family took it back, trading as Ratgoed Slate Quarries with D.H. Rees managing, but when he died in 1932 and D.E. Jones took over, manpower was down to a dozen. A few men were taken on during the late 30s, but the war brought a sharp decline and by 1945, J. Hughes only had 3 men under him (with a wage bill, including his own of £20 per week!). By early 1946 Miss Helene Lewis faced the inevitable and closed.

Description

Disturbed geology and lack of planning led to complicated working and movement of material.

The early, mostly open, workings near valley floor level were actually on the Broad Vein, the main, Narrow Vein workings were on 8 levels, in a compact area, high on the hillside. The upper workings, down to 5 level, were mainly open. Originally material was brought down to the mill on the valley floor by a long incline, which, after the building of the later, intermediate inclines, became redundant. A second, Upper mill was built on 6 level to increase capacity. It was used latterly just for rough sawing. A barracks adjoined it.

The last mill to be built, Middle mill, was on 8 Level, it sawed and planed material brought out on that level. Curiously, 7 level, due to subsequent tipping, became inaccessible to a mill and thus its adit only handled rubbish. 8 adit on the other hand had no chambering and only served two vertical shafts in which block was lowered from 7. The lowest mill eventually became to some extent redundant, but it is believed that latterly some fine finishing was done there.

All mills were Pelton wheel powered, but after the 1936 dam failure, an oil engine was installed in the middle mill, presumably this was then the only one remaining in use. Mains electricity was never available.

Adjacent to the lowest mill, was a tiny but self-contained community with dwellings, a chapel and a shop. The chapel closed about 1936, because, legend has it, the Lewis' quarrelled with the minister!

The Meirionethshire Mines Report of 1892 shows both the highest and lowest adits as being at 1048' which suggests level 6 being the only one then in use. Oddly the 1901 25" O.S. shows this quarry (and Cymerau) as disused whereas the 6" does not.

Remains

Afforestation makes interpretation difficult. The highest level (1), above the forestry road, is a tiny open working. Level 2, alongside the road, is a short adit, breaking out into Level 1.

Below is a large pit working, divided into three parts. In the face is a large adit, (Level 3) reached by a shelved tramway. Level 4 has largely been quarried away. At Level 5 is the cutting access to the pit, there is some underground chambering off and workings break up from below.

On Level 6 there are several dressing sheds and other buildings including the Upper mill, a double structure, basically built of country rock, but modified with sawn-ends. Though much degraded, there is evidence of overhead shafting. There is a weigh-house and other buildings and vestiges of what must have been the barracks. Men living in say Corris, would walk daily to work, those living much further afield would lodge here from Monday to Saturday.

At Level 7 is an adit (collapsed) which leads to chambering, which breaks out into the pit workings. An isolated rubbish run emerges from this adit, it is possible that after subsequent tipping isolated this adit, a wire rope was used to bring blocks up Level 6.

On Level 8 is Middle mill which has the base of an i.c. engine, either for mill power or for a compressor, and most interestingly, an elaborately roofed stairway leading down to the Pelton wheel pit. Near the mill are some building foundations and a stocking area. There are several rubbish runs at this level emanating from an adit some 200 yards long, cut through country rock, with no workings but with 2 vertical shafts dropping from the chambering above. There is rail in situ.

The incline system is unusually complex and varied for what was in all honesty a small quarry. The short 5-6 incline seems to have had a horizontal sheave. The 6-7 incline, with a nice flight of steps alongside, has traces of an underfloor sheave.

Of the other 4 inclines, all of the table type, the oldest seems to be the 7-Down, which is near the northern boundary of the site. It has a semi-circular structure at its head, probably for a horizontal sheave. Part way down is a most delightful powder house with "air bricks" formed out of drilled slate and traces of the wooden flooring. This probably went out of use when adit 7 became isolated or when Middle mill was built.

Middle mill was fed by 2 inclines 5-8 and 6-8, both with conventional drums. The former has unusual and complex brake gear with the band running in a flanged ring. The drum (7' dia. x 6' long) is in two separate parts, collapsed but virtually complete. The 6-8 has a drumhouse repaired by building new walls inside the old and shortening the drum.

From Level 8, a further incline, (now cut by a forestry road), runs down to the valley floor. The drum gear (also remote type) is similar to the 5-8 and 6-8 inclines, but although the brake has a shaft to couple up a second brake, and there is a spare band on the ground, there does not seem to have been space for a second brake drum. The remote brake lever was abandoned and replaced by a direct operating lever with a very crude wooden pin-down pillar, suggesting the possibility of conversion to table operation. There is a further powder house on this incline.

By the 1880s only the 5-6, 6-8 & 8-down inclines were apparently in use, and in the final years only the 8-down.

Near the foot of both lower inclines, are buildings, some apparently adaptions of pre-existing structures.

There are several ruined buildings at valley floor level, including the original mill with some evidence of underfloor shafting and embedded in the ground is the table of a saw-bench, and curious "A" frame fabrication.

Close above this are some small, open pit workings and also a flooded adit with a possible short incline, these may well be the original workings. They do not feature on later quarry plans.

Along the tramroad from the lower mills area, are the ruins of a row of 4 cottages, (the end one was a shop), the chapel and between them the site of a manse, all 5 dwellings served by a double lavatory over the stream nearby. In front are ruins of the manager's house, complete with lavatory, served by the same brook as, (but downstream of!) the communal convenience. Ratgoed Hall, the owner's residence, is still in occupation. In front of the Hall is a most elaborately ornate stable block.

Section 7, CWM LLEFENNI

This delightful valley was the scene, on and off for 60 years, of attempts to exploit the Broad Vein. The one "big" quarry was Cambergi, a brave and ambitious attempt to work somewhat doubtful rock. The other quarries were little more than trials mainly by the Griffiths family. Large were the expectations, small was the success, even into the 1920s the area was being hyped as offering great opportunities. They form an astonishing example of how hope can triumph over both sense and experience through successive generations.

CAMBERGI SH765108 (40)

Also known as Wenallt, worked the Broad Vein.

In 1873 the Cambergi Slate Quarry Company was formed, mainly by Pontypool men, one of whom, D. Williams may have been the David Williams, who was then a director of Pontypool Iron & Tin Plate Co. Ltd. They leased the land from the Anwyl family, laid out extensive workings, built a fine mill and a magnificent incline.

This considerable, but unwise, expenditure quickly exhausted company's funds, and in 1875 the lease was surrendered. The Anwyls immediately issued a fresh one to Sarah Griffiths and her daughter Elizabeth. It was for 39 years at £10 pa merging to a royalty of 1/6 (7.5p) per ton for first quality slates and 1/ (5p) per ton, for seconds and slab. Elizabeth's brother Griffith William Griffiths, had been quarrying on a small scale at Fronfraith, at the top of the valley for about ten years, and faced with lack of success and strained relations with his partner John Hughes Jones, he must have been overjoyed at getting his hands on this well-equipped quarry.

By 1877, finding Cambergi's rock did not match the excellence of its equipment, he started digging on the other side of the valley at Hengae.

In 1883, short of capital, he explored the possibility of mortgaging or selling Cambergi.

Inventories in connection with these mortgage applications and sale offers include 1530 yards of bridge rail & 100 yards of flat rail, with 20 loose rail bars. 2 Sampson cranes with chains & legs. 9

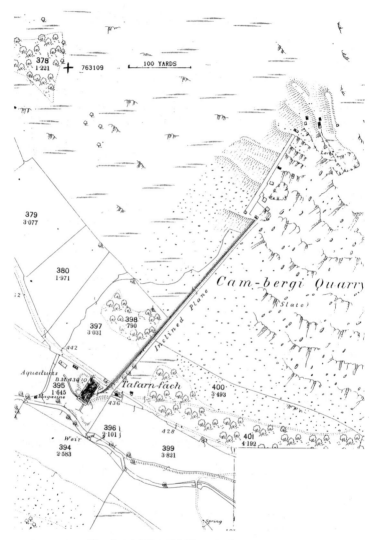

Cambergi (Wenallt) Slate Quarry, 1st O.S.
By kind permission National Library of Wales.

sheet iron trams & 3 incomplete (rubbish wagons). 2 sets of turnout plates, 6 weighing machines, 8 block trucks, 6 slate wagons. 1 small winch with Cast Iron frame and chains, 2 "strong" winches with chains. 6 Cast Iron turntables. 1 incline drum, 5' diameter at upper incline. 1 incline drum 6' diameter at middle incline, 1 incline drum 8' diameter at lower incline & 76 cast iron incline rollers with stands. Various wire ropes, 6 Slate Dressing benches and a host of timbers etc. Quarrying tools included mallets, splitting chisels, hammers, cast iron drills of various lengths, crowbars, jumpers, pikes (?) & spades.

At the mill were a water wheel 30' diameter, 9 Owen patent sawing machines, 1 planing machine, 1 saw sharpening machine, 1 grinding stone, 10 India-rubber belts. There were also carpenter's, smiths tool and horse tack. 36lb of candles, 210 coils of tape fuse, 50lbs of powder, 200 squares of glass 5-10 x 1-1 each (the rooflights of slate mills were constantly shattered by stray debris from blasting).

There is an undated and unaddressed report on the quarry by Robert Williams, probably from this time. He noted that the "Narrow Gauge Railway" runs within four to five hundred yards. He described the Broad Vein as having "proved itself at Abercwmeiddaw to be the best Vein in the neighbourhood", and that Cambergi "embraces an unusual length of the Slate or Slab rock" which he praised for its colour and quality. He emphasised the "elevated ground" as lending itself to gallery working and the abundant source of water power, "having a strong and extensive Reservoir already made, and a good stream of water runs into it, sufficient to supply the works and keep them regularly going all the year round".

Oddly, having said that it lent itself to gallery working, he went on to criticise that method of working, saying it should have been chambered underground, and if this was done it "would be one of the most profitable concerns in the district".

It would be perhaps unfair to point out that Williams left the managership of Bryneglwys quarry following sharp criticism of his working or that his subsequent post at Abercwmeiddaw was of very short duration!

Griffiths was not able to sell but did get a loan and was selling roofing slates from Cambergi in 1886, but shortly after this he closed down and sold some of the machinery. Local legend is that boundary disputes with Aberllefenni caused closure, but no document has been found to confirm this. However if the wall which runs through the site is the Aberllefenni boundary, then virtually all the actual extraction was on the Aberllefenni land!

By 1887 Griffiths was being pressed by the North & South Wales Bank for monies secured on land in Machynlleth. He got involved with Edward Wood and John A. Talbot, to whom he hoped to sell Cambergi, but this fell through, with some acrimony.

The next year there were other problems. Firstly, Griffiths was also in partnership with J.H. Jones as Timber merchants and Jones had successfully sued him for a debt. Secondly there were quarrels with his sister Elizabeth and brother Reginald. Elizabeth, besides wanting her share of the proceeds of the sale of plant was demanding £700 as her share of the family house. He borrowed £50 from Reginald to keep Elizabeth quiet and attempted to make over to her his share of the timber business, which upset Jones who in 1890 was still demanding monies owed. There were numerous other debts, mainly for small amounts, for goods and services, but totalling almost £2000.

Several debts were to other quarries, mostly trifling sums, e.g. Abercwmeiddaw Slate Quarry £1.15.9 (£1.78) & 11/2 (55p), R.D. Pryce of Aberllefenni 3/4 (16p), Liquidators of Abercorris £7.18.0 (£7.90), Braich Goch £2.14.11 (£2.75), J. Williams (Rhiw'r Gwreiddyn) £8.11.9 (£8.59). These undoubtedly were for small items "borrowed", not uncommon amongst small businesses operating in remote areas even today, but suggesting financial stringency. In fact Griffiths did eventually clear what he owed, but it took him until 1902 to do so.

In 1896 C.G. Crowden expressed an interest in buying both Cambergi and Hengae and got J.H. Roberts to report. Roberts said Cambergi had been productive of slate and slab for many years, with extensive extraction of the outcrop which had been worked to the Aberllefenni boundary (!), and that a portion on the 3rd floor immediately above the top of incline remained. If the "machine house", which was well-planned with a capacity for 12 machines, with ample water supply from a reservoir "constructed at great cost", was put in proper repair, it could again be utilised. He regretted that the previous company, who had expended much time and capital, had tipped over the vein, but that underground working should be considered. The existence of the 400 yard incline, with wire-rope was mentioned. He said that there was another vein higher up the valley.

This report apparently did not cause Mr Crowden to part with his cash, but it did encourage Griffiths to pay £200 to renew the lease. In 1897 John Lewis, who had succeeded Williams at Abercwmeiddaw, was asked for another report.

He too, referred to the possibility of extending the "Narrow Gauge Railway right to the yard of the Machine House, giving communication via Machynlleth to any part of the country or to Aberdovey for Shipment". He praised the quality of the rock, describing it as "Silver Grey" with excellent Foot Joints, Back Joints and Cleavage.

He too, "quite disagreed with the attempt made to work the property as an Open Quarry", stating that "thousands of pounds could have been saved by working underground in chambers, leaving good strong pillars between each chamber to keep the roof up".

He described the first gallery (from the bottom), as having a tunnel driven through into an open space, where there was a "large body of good solid rock which would yield thousands of tons of rough blocks to be manufactured into Slates and Slabs of merchantable sizes". He suggested that a start could be made there, with clearance and repairs to the incline costing only £80 — £100, pending the opening of chambers.

He noted the presence of "Iron Rubbish Wagons, Crane, Chains, Blocks, Rails, Weighing Machines, and Cars to run up and down the incline to convey blocks". The buildings were itemised as; — Machine House 98'4 x 42', with ample room to put up 12 or 14 tables with "a good strong Water Wheel", Blacksmith Shop, Magazine and Office.

Boldly he asserted that being on the same vein as Abercwmeiddaw Quarry, was a great recommendation, and that if it were to be worked underground in chambers properly and economically, it would become "one of the best profitable Quarries in the district".

Griffiths' having failed to sell, did some occasional work, for a time.

In 1920, at the height of the post-war boom G.W. Griffiths' grandson Edward, offered for sale Cambergi, Hengae and the other works in the valley, 1168 acres in all. Again the obligatory report was commissioned, this time from Evan Hughes F.G.S., M.I.M.E.

With the optimism customary in such reports, he described how the area had been worked for 150 years, that the slate was well exposed, with a 55° dip and with right-angled cleavage, praising the 160 yard Broad Vein for its "fine quality, high percentage yield and great thickness". He mentioned that at neighbouring Aberllefenni very large profits had been returned for 120 years, and that fine slabs could be seen there "daily", (but omitted to say that Aberllefenni was on the Narrow Vein!)

He described the "great amount of work already done", at Cambergi. The 1st gallery had been worked down into a pit to the floor of the 2nd to the extent of 63' x 84' x 48', and that good slate had been obtained from this pit when the quarry was last worked "40 years ago". The dimensions of galleries 4,5,6 & 7, were respectively given as — 66' x 38' x 54', 46' x 50' x 51', 70' x 51' x 54', & 63' x 84' x 54'.

He alleged "great demand for Brewer's Cisterns and Billiards Tables", prices of up to £12-£14 per ton being cited. The quality of 24 x 12 slates left on site was remarked on and it was said the galleries might be extended (further into Aberllefenni property!) and that another, lower gallery might be opened, the incline bed being ready to have rails re-laid.

He mentioned the convenience of the Corris Railway and the possibility of extending it up the valley. Costs to rail-head being estimated at 5/ (25p) per ton. The Dead Rent of £50 pa merging to a tonnage royalty of 3/- (15p) for best, 2/6 (12.5p) for seconds & 2/- (10p) for thirds, was described as modest.

Water Power was most ambitiously dealt with. Hughes estimated that even in the dry season 500hp would be available, at a suggested generating station site at the base of Cwmbychan near Hengae farm. The Cwmbychan stream could provide 100hp via a reservoir and a 400 yard, 16 degree, 1000 gallons per minute, pipe. A further pipeline from the Llefenni, would give 3-4000 gallons per minute at a head sufficient for 500hp.

An electric installation would either have a 100hp unit on the

Cwmbychan stream and a 400hp unit on the main stream or 2 x 250hp units on the combined streams. It was suggested that as fuel costs were £30 per hp per annum, the value of power would be £15,000 a year. Surplus power could be used to light the neighbouring villages.

Enamelling, "for which there is a growing demand", was suggested as an ancilliary industry, using electric ovens and utilising quarry waste. Crushing mills to pulverise waste would, it was said, produce a clear profit of "at least" 10/ (50p) per ton.

The property could be worked as 4 quarries but economies would result from making it one big concern.

It was optimistically instanced that on the basis of annual output averaging 35 tons per man, costs would only be £6.10.0 (£6.50) per ton raised, and with slate fetching £11 per ton 1000 men would bring in a gross profit of £157,500 each year.

Even after deducting Royalties of 2/6 (12.5p) per ton and carriage and loading at 9/ (45p) per ton and allowing £8000 for repairs and renewals, £5000 for administration, £10,000 for rates and taxes, £5000 for the depreciation of the lease and £15,000 for contingencies, a net profit of £94,425 would result. This did not include the £6000 that the auxilliary industries would bring in.

Hughes concluded by suggesting that this was "a most valuable property and the biggest slate proposition ever to be put before the public".

Griffiths failed to sell, but undoubtely encouraged by the report, sought advice from Jonathan Davies of Porthmadog, about the chances of seeking capital and floating a company himself. Davies replied that it was a bad time and that investors were not putting money into slate. The tone of the letter gently infers that in any case it would be too big a job for Griffiths to tackle. No further work was done at Cambergi, but Griffiths continued to do some work himself at some of his smaller sites.

The building of a forestry road to near the top of the site in the late 1980s makes it possible that we have not heard the last of Cambergi.

Description

Hillside terraces were boldly developed on 9 levels with an incline down to the valley floor where there was a water powered mill. Generally working was on the south side and tipping on the north side, with tentative attempts to go underground. The 1883 listing shows no trimming machines as all Roofing Slate was produced by hand on the terraces, the Mill being solely used for the sawing of slab.

Product was carted to Aberllefenni, for loading onto the C.R.

Remains

The obvious feature is the spectacular but much degraded incline down from the workings, it is in four pitches, with several ruined drumhouses, the middle two being remote type, it served 7 levels, which were clearly originally neatly laid out.

Dressing sheds are on the various levels. Some working was also done on 2 levels above the top most incline level. There are traces of a possibly uncompleted incline to serve these.

At valley floor the ruins of the well-built mill is of great interest. There are 4 belt-slots in the floor, serving, in pairs, the original 9 saws and one planer. There is massive underfloor tunnel for the drive shaft, and behind and below the mill the pit for the water wheel. There is a leat from a reservoir some distance up valley (later rebuilt and reused by Aberllefenni quarry) and a particularly fine tunnel taking the tailrace to the river. There is a dwelling/office building and along a short tramway formation, remains of a storage shed at a dock for loading carts. The short working life is confirmed by the paucity of mill waste. There are a number of finished and part-finished slabs around.

The nearby, sadly ruined, Blue Cottages with their slate-fenced allotments and pair of lavatories (2 for the whole row!), some distance in front, were for Aberllefenni workers.

CWM YR HENGAE SH761103 (35)

Trial, date not known but probably around turn of the century, undoubtedly by the Griffiths', unlikely that much if any, saleable product came out.

Description

A couple of trial adits.

Remains

Adits collapsed, with tipping down hillside. No traces of buildings.

FOTY Y WAUN SH761128 (36)

Also known as Y Waun or Waunllefenni.

Unsuccessful working possibly dating from around 1870, some limited production. The 1890 O.S. map shows it as disused. Revived, briefly in 1934 by Edward Griffiths with 3 men.

Description

Small open pit, possibly with some underground work.

Remains

Large rubbish tip. Vestiges of a dressing shed. Traces of an access track.

FRON FRAITH SH759125 & 757121 (29)

Shortly after a Mining Journal report of 1865, that "A new discovery of slate had been made to the north of Aberllefenni", G.W. Griffiths and J.H. Jones obtained a lease, from Thomas Llewelyn Anwyl for rights to extract slates, construct buildings etc. They also were to be authorised to build a (3 mile!) tramway over Hengae & Cambergi. Digging was commenced, apparently at 759125, but results proved disappointing and Griffiths must have been glad, ten years later to seize the opportunity to transfer his energies to Cambergi.

Little more was heard of this until 1920 when Evan Hughes made his report on the prospects of the whole of the valley. He defined the Fron Fraith Beds as being an 80 yard and a 400 yard bed, separated by a hard band. Stream erosion had apparently provided a good exposure in the 80 yard bed, showing a blue colour and good joints. On the 400 yard bed he said that 2 adit levels had been driven for 25 yard, one being "roofed" to the surface providing a chamber 20 yards deep, where he had seen extracted a block of deep blue colour which split down to "8 to the inch". The absence of joints would call for a channelling machine, but large blocks could be "immediately and prosperously extracted".

This must have prompted Edward Griffiths, grandson of G.W. to resume, at least some exploratory work.

At 757121 there was certainly no working until a late date, nothing is shown on pre WW1 O.S. maps, it is believed that following the 1920 Hughes report Griffiths investigated the "80 yard bed" at this point.

Description (at 759125)

Two adits in tandem, with some limited underground chambering.

Remains

Just on the edge of forestry, two adits, open but wet, ruins of a dressing shed, with CGI roof on the lower level. Some trimming waste.

Description (at 757121)

1 or 2 tunnels, one at least, roofed out to the surface.

Remains

One, or possibly two, run-in levels are just discernable, and evidence of a collapse from one. Very much overgrown rubbish runs.

A curious square building with central pillar, (which is shown on 1891 O.S.) has sawn ends, and lengths of bridge rail alongside. The nearby small reservoir and leat are seemingly not associated with this working.

HENGAE SH759115 (31)

This small underground working, had high hopes and even higher recommendations but little good rock came out.

An Anwyl family settlement of 1875 refers to slate quarrying. If it is this site which was referred to, then extraction had taken place prior to Thomas Anwyl granting Griffith William Griffiths, a £10 pa Take Note in 1877. Griffiths already discouraged at Cambergi, did not do much better here. However when in 1896, J.H. Roberts reporting to a C.G. Crowden on this and Cambergi, stated that there was "an inexhaustible" potential within the Hengae portion, Griffiths was stirred to renew his Take Note.

The report from about the same time by John Lewis of Abercwmeiddaw praised the potential, mentioning the advantages of the 150 yard width of the Broad Vein, the "Silver Grey" colour and the economy with which it could be developed, saying that a level could be driven for only 50/0 (£2.50) per yard. He suggested that if the "Machine House" at Cambergi (then idle), were used "great profits" would ensue. He referred to the "opening that had been made on the western side at Hengae, where a block had been split in his presence into layers 1/8 thick". It was suggested that 5 or 6 galleries might be opened to provide fine slate for a century or more.

In 1897, in the course of negotiations between Mrs Anwyl and A.R. Pryce of Aberllefenni for water rights, (to use the old

Cambergi reservoir for powering a compressor). Griffiths was mentioned as being in possession, a lease renewal for 40 years being confidently anticipated.

Mrs Anwyl's assumption was premature, Griffiths declined to pay the £30 premium for the lease, but did agree to pay a dead rent of £20, merging into the usual 1/6 (7.5p) on first grade slates and 1/- (5p) on seconds and slab, on a continuing Take Note basis.

In fact in 1904 when the Take Note renewal came up, he sought a reduction in the dead rent. The formidable Mrs Eleanor Anwyl, widow of Thomas declined, complaining of the disrepair of the buildings, and at the loss she was sustaining through Griffiths' "failure to properly work the quarry".

G.W. Griffiths died later that year leaving his property mainly to his eldest son Sidney Joseph Griffiths but with a specific mention that his other son, Alexander Robert Griffiths, should have the quarry. It would appear that he derived little advantage from this legacy.

In 1920 this "valuable" quarry was still being offered for sale, by Edward Griffiths along with Cambergi and rights for the whole of the upper valley.

The Evan Hughes report mentioned the grey Hengae beds, which he described as a series extending for 1000 yards, where "no trials had been done but an exposure in a stream-bed had yielded a good block" and driving 2 or 3 test levels was advised. There were no takers.

Description

One or possibly two adits, leading to chambering.

Remains

The forestry road, which initially follows the line of the access track, has obliterated any dressing shed or the like. Similarly, planting may have concealed another adit besides the flooded one which remains.

Some distance away, north of Hengae farm are some ruined structures, one of which might have been for slate sawing. Around is a quantity of good quality Slab and some Cistern sections, so it may be that these are the buildings whose condition upset Mrs Anwyl.

MYNYDD Y WAUN SH763132 (38)

Shown as disused on 1890 O.S. Doubtful if any saleable product ever came out.

Description
Virtually just a trial adit.

Remains
Excavation and quite large tip. Now in forestry.

Section 8 THE QUARRIES OF THE DULAS VALLEY

These were a number of scattered workings, seeking material from isolated occurences, remote from the main veins, and in some cases a long way from roads or dwellings. At times of high prices there were always those prepared to back their optimism and dig in the most unlikely places.

Llwyngwern was the only substantial and long-lasting commercial enterprise, Rhiw'r Gwreiddyn, hampered by a lack of rail connection, much less so. At Ceinws serious operations commenced 15/20 years too late. Apart from these, the lonely but fascinating Darren quarry was the only one ever developed.

The rest were tiny, ephemeral workings, most of which produced little or nothing.

AFON DULAS SH749029 (20)
Underground, almost certainly only a trial.
Description
Just a single adit.
Remains
Trace of possible adit.

BRYN LLWYD SH753071 (26)
Underground, very small, only some building stone and some poor quality roofing slate was produced.

J.A. Williams speaks of loads being smashed in transit. Bowen Jones writing in 1905 said that it had been worked for about six years by Evan Reese. The Inspector of Mines report for 1903 shows 3 men employed but the 1904 & 1905 reports recorded it as idle, Jones confirmed this in 1907.
Description
Probably just a single adit.
Remains
Some ground disturbance, but the immediate site has been levelled.

BRYN LLWYD UCHAF SH748073 (18)
A small trial on Braich Goch property, presumably to test the extent of the "Appendix" Vein. Almost certainly never produced.

Description
A single adit.
Remains
Adit, open.

CEINWS BACH SH762060 (37)

There is some possibility that there was some testing of rock here.
Description
Some outcrop material may have been dug.
Remains
Nothing positively identified.

COED Y FFRIDD SH747030 (16)

A slightly more substantial working than most and certainly did produce some roofing slate.
Description
Small pit working.
Remains
Pit with tunnel access (run in). No buildings but some trimming waste. Well defined cart track.

CWM GLODDFA SH766062 (41) ERA SH760064 (33) ESCAIRGEILIOG MILL SH759059 (30)

These two quarries and a mill must be looked at together since their function and ownership were intertwined. They are also collectively known as Ceinws.

The Cambria Wynne Slate Quarry Company was formed in 1870 by Lord Paget, William C. Hallet and others, to take over an established digging at Cwm Gloddfa otherwise known as Cwmodyn, (this latter name is also used locally for Abercorris quarry).

By 1875 they had exhausted their resources mainly on converting the old Grist mill, and putting in saws, planers and enamelling capacity, which was quite out of scale with the limited potential of the quarry. They built a branch connection and bridge from the mill to the Corris Railway, but never completed the planned tramway connection between quarry and mill.

Although the quarry was on doubtful ground, the same Vein was, rightly, thought to be more promising on the other side of the valley. In 1878 with this prospect and the opportunity to buy the lot including the fine, well equipped mill at the bargain price of £850, David Jones and Evan Reese stepped in, and abandoning serious work at Cwm Gloddfa, started work at Era quarry, (locally known as Colorado). They traded as the Cambria Wynne Plain & Enamelled Slate Co. They were reputed to have employed up to 50 men, but the outputs of well below 1000 tons pa suggest a number were engaged in enamelling or other processes.

Evan Reese had worked with his father as a Watchmaker, before branching out, in 1868 as a "Wheeler and Dealer" in property, particularly mines, first as a go-between, then on his own account. Variously described as Auctioneer and Mining Agent. He now fancied his chances as a slate magnate.

In 1880, David Jones having seemingly dropped out, Reese sold off the mill to John Rowlands, (a solicitor of Machynlleth), who ran it as the Dulas Enamelling Works and Quarry Co. Jeremiah Williams of Rhiw'r Gwreiddyn quarry also having some interest. It was possibly at this time that the mill was extended.

In 1884 Evan Reese, got Rowlands to put him in charge of the mill, and the following year embarked on his grand scheme. This was to merge the mill, his Era quarry and the Rhiw'r Gwreiddyn quarry, which was to be linked to the mill by a tramway. As Era quarry now was.

This would have made sense as Rhiw'r Gwreiddyn product was being trundled by road to be railed at Escairgeiliog mill and some Rhiw'r Gwreiddyn block was probably being reduced there anyway.

It was a bold and imaginative plan, although his proposal to charge the Corris Railway rent for the use of the river bridge, was less intelligent and met with a dusty answer.

In 1887 Reese agreed to buy back the mill from Rowlands for £2300 plus £700 for stock & debts (stock included 150 "Chimney pieces"), but actually seems to have only paid the £200 deposit. He made similar arrangements with Jeremiah Williams of Rhiw'r Gwreiddyn and had tentative wayleaves over the land for the proposed tramway. If he could hold the lot together and sell it on, he would make a killing.

He sought the good offices of William Roberts of Birmingham, agreeing to pay him £800 if he could introduce a buyer. Roberts brought in J.H. Hutton, who, apparently, was prepared to buy the whole outfit for £9000. Reese paid Roberts his commission, but Hutton alleging, undoubtedly correctly, that matters had been misrepresented to him, cried off and sued Reese for £500.

Roberts then said he would take a half interest himself, but temporising over the matter of payment, moved in on Reese and took a hand in the management of the mill, which they were now calling the Dulas Slate Company. Roberts insisted that new equipment was required, which he ordered, apparently in Reese's name. He also helped out by taking care of the money side of things which seems to have meant that he looked after cash received, whilst the invoices for purchases went to Reese!

The whole thing came unstuck and in 1889, and with Rowlands still unpaid, Reese was declared bankrupt, owing almost £4,000 with assets of under £600. He blamed his misfortunes on Roberts profligate spending. Rhiw'r Gwreiddyn quarry was taken on by W.J. Lewis, but its proposed rail connection was never built.

The redoubtable Reese carried on working Era quarry in his wife's name, trading as the Fronfelen Slate & Slab Quarries. The Dulas Slate company which was still working the Escairgeiliog mill failed in 1891 and the following year Frances Reese took over their lease. When Evan was granted his discharge from bankruptcy, he joined her in the company, and in 1897 the couple were the main sponsors in floating the Era Welsh Slate Quarries Ltd. The company was to take over Era quarry and the mill and to exploit Reese's Patent School Slates. They seem to have been successful for a time, employing 84 men in 1898.

By 1908, with Evan Reese again having "cashflow" problems, John Rowlands had regained possession, but the company was being pursued by the National Provincial Bank, for £325.13.5 (£325.67). The Bank obtained judgement and it ceased trading.

H.H. Badham, then obtained the lease which included several houses and cottages for £2,000. Reese then came back in the frame again and undertook to buy him out, but Badham could not get Reese to complete the purchase, he could not even get him to pay the £100 owing for the option, let alone the £200 undertaken as compensation for the delay, nor even a nominal fiver for "Sporting Rights".

No wonder, for Reese had entered into the agreement in

confident anticipation of re-selling the lot together with Braich Goch & Gaewern to the General United Slate Company Ltd, at considerable profit, a sale which, of course never took place.

The Bank was now chasing Reese for the monies he owed, and were unimpressed by the assurance that £100 would immediately be forthcoming when he got his £2,000 down payment from General United. He was also being pressed by Long the landlord of the Ceinws rail branch, for deadrent.

All this was an "action replay" of events of 1889. Reese appears to have been a persuasive man as he had borrowed money and cashed dud cheques all up and down the Dulas valley, to finance his various adventures which also included trials at Tarran Cadian, and some unsuccessful working at Bryn Llwyd.

By the end of 1908 Reese was again bankrupt, owing over £3,000, mainly to traders and local worthies, including John Rowlands, as well as several banks, all of whom eventually agreed to accept 7/6 (37.5p) in the pound.

The quarry survived even if Reese did not. In 1909 D.E. Jones formed the New Era Slate Quarry, restarted the next year with 10 men, doubling this by the time the outbreak of war brought closure.

H. Redford's Ceinws Slate Company, took over in early 1920 but it was a short lived venture as was the Anglo-Welsh Enamelled Slate Co.

Description, Cwm Gloddfa Quarry

Two small open diggings in a constricted little valley, shown on the O.S. as two quarries, presumably reflecting the Hallet and the pre-Hallet eras. Material was removed via a short incline, and with cartage to the Escairgeiliog mill.

Remains, Cwm Gloddfa Quarry

Some rubbish runs and several collapsed adits that seem to have been unsuccessful trials. There is a curious drumhouse with an outcrop of rock forming one wall, with the brakeman's platform cut into a ledge. The route of the proposed tramway to the mill is obvious.

Description, Era Quarry

Open working, on 3 levels connected by an incline. Material was trammed to the mill at Escairgeiliog.

Remains, Era Quarry
Very degraded, little other than the incline and tramway formation to the mill.
Description, Escairgeiliog Mill
A substantial traditional mill building, with water-turbine power for saws and planers, supplied by a launder from a take-off point upstream. Also had enamelling equipment. Connected to the Corris Railway by the Ceinws quarries branch.
Remains, Escairgeiliog Mill
The mill complex is largely intact although only the rough-stone walls of the original building stand. The extension, of sawn-end construction, is in re-use, and represents and excellent example of a typical integrated slate quarry mill of the smaller kind. The Corris Railway branch, with the collapsed timber bridge, is obvious, but the launder has vanished.

DARREN SH721058 & 723057 (2)

This is shown on the O.S. map as two separate quarries, also known as Tarren y Gesail and as Darren y Gesail and as Cambria Wynne, (because of that company's attempt to re-develop it). Although small it was of complex geology.

At 723057, handily located on an ancient route, there may have been some very early working. In the 1850s Lawrence Ruck cut an adit into the pre-existing pit and put up a mill and other buildings. An O.J. Hughes was named as agent (manager).

The iron content made the slate difficult to sell and work was abandoned. A further attempt was made at lower level in the hope that a better product would result but this was little more successful. Subsequently there was some small scale working on the opposite side of the hill, at 721058, but quality apart, the lack of water for power and the near impossibility of transport made this site a very doubtful proposition.

There is a report that billiards tables were produced, 9' x 4' & 12' x 6', which even in the usual 5 sections, (up to 4 cwt apiece), without power and 3 miles from decent transport would call for some dedication.

A report of 1878 by William Evans to Elwyn Jones described there being 3 Veins, Big or Llewellyn, Cadwgan & Pyritous. On the first named there being a level 80 yards long and 35 yards below it a second adit 220 yards long. Also a 150 yard east-west level "on the other side of the hill". On the Cadwgan side there was said to be a trial level westward and an open patch. Evans said that slate had been won on the Drainllwydion side and suggests that the Pyritic below "could be patched".

Following this David Jones, partner with Evan Reese in the Cambria Wynne quarry took an interest and sought a wayleave for a tramway over Cwm Cadian farm, but he did little if any, work.

Bowen Jones writing in 1905, described it as "Two large openings connected by an adit level, with old buildings and 2 hand-powered sawing tables". He stated that the late Lawrence Ruck had spent £11-15,000 there and that there were several tons of slabs and some rough slate on the site. He described the slate as "banded" but of good "metal". He quoted an Owen Owen as saying that in the last 34 years a few men had got slates from there to mend roofs but that 35-40 years before, 5 or 6 men worked there. He referred to David Jones of Escairgeiliog as having had some interest.

Description

There were two distinct sites, the southerly one, Drainllwydion, Ruck's initial work, consisted of a large pit accessed by an adit, with a hand powered saw mill and other buildings, apparently producing mainly roofing slate. Later another adit was driven below this with a sawing mill, also without power source, where mainly Slab was produced.

On the other side, the later work was much less orderly, partly open, partly underground, roofing slate only being made, with no mechanisation.

Remains

The pit is accessed by a flooded adit, (the 80 yard adit mentioned by Evans?). A tramway formation leads to a rake of contiguous buildings, comprising, from west to east; a saw house 20' x 15' containing fragments of an 7'4" x 5'4" saw table. Then a 12' x 15' space containing some unidentified iron artifacts. Next along there is a 20' building with access towards the adit where perhaps blocks were first brought, then a 6' wide passage that may have been the space for a rubbish-run track. Then a 10' x 8' open-fronted building (splitting shed?) which contains a quantity of part-finished slab, finally an office of similar size. In front is a large stocking area on built-up waste, partitioned by the usual low wall.

This stocking area was clearly inadequate for the huge stock which had built up when work was abandoned as apart from the thousands of slates stacked there, thousands more are on the open hillside around. Typical of them would be a 16 x 8, (Lady) severely banded and rather degraded, averaging 0.27″ thick. There are also some sawn ends around, but almost none in the buildings.

Below is a further adit (Evans 220 yard adit?), flooded but with through draught (to pit?). Close by is a building of about 10′ x 16′ containing a shaft about 10′ long with a 4′ diameter flywheel at one end and a cast gear-wheel at its centre. There are sawn ends in this building and some around about. There is very little mill or dressing waste. Adjacent is a dressing-shed. There is some Slab, of reasonable quality, and a number of slates on a stocking area alongside. The 10″ x 7″s (Narrow Ladies) are in better condition and bluer, though coarser than the ones from the upper adit, thicknesses are uneven, varying from 0.33″ to 0.28″.

On the northern side there is a flooded, apparently blind adit running south west (the 150 yard?) with some open working above. Immediately to the north, and at a higher level with a trackway between is a short, also flooded, adit that breaks out to bank, with a dressing shed nearby. There is a small third adit. There are a number of slates lying about, dark in colour with heavy iron content and inclusions. Most are 16″ x 8″ around 0.28″ thick. Apparently no Slab (and precious little roofing slate) was produced on this northern side.

Unusually, for such a remote site, there are no barracks or dwellings. the modernised house between the Corris Railway and the river just to the north of Lliwdy halt is reputed to be Ruck's office for the quarry.

DOLYDDERWEN SH750029 (21)

Very much a "vernacular" site, may have only produced building block, handiness of situation compensating for poorness of product.

Description

Tiny hillside quarry.

Remains
Working face alongside main road.

GLANDULAS SH751038 (23)
Very tiny, again poor stuff but handy to get at. Llwyngwern quarry was also known by this name.
Description
Minute roadside digging.
Remains
Almost nothing.

GOEDWIG SH752063 (24)
It is unlikely that any saleable product emerged.
Description
Almost certainly just a single adit.
Remains
Lost in forestry.

GOEDWIG WEST SH745066 (13)
Trial only.
Description
Appears as a single trial level on O.S. maps.
Remains
In forestry.

HAFOTTY SH725064 (Also known as Tap Llwyd) (3)
An unsuccessful trial of around 1860 by Lawrence Ruck (of Darren quarry).
Description
Underground, Excavation with adit driven to it.
Remains
Some possible ground disturbance in forestry.

LLWYNGWERN SH757045 (Also known as Glandulas) (28)
As early as 1835, Simon Cock of Llwyngwern is listed as a "Slate proprietor", but its nearness to the old road suggests it may have been in use well before this.

The Mining Journal of November 1853 described it as "a long-neglected quarry now re-opened by W.R. Williams of

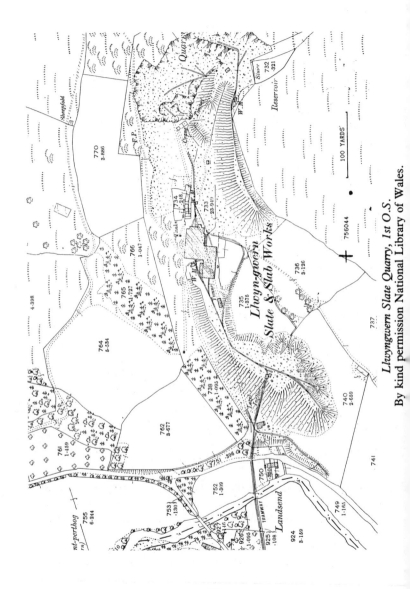

Llwyngwern Slate Quarry, 1st O.S.
By kind permission National Library of Wales.

126

Dolgelley, having a 30′ water-wheel and saws and planers supplied by H. Owen of Caernarvon".

A price list for that year survives, — Gravestones @ £3.7.8 (£3.38). Mangers @ 10/ (50p). Pigsties @ 2/6 (12.5p) "Slips" (small slabs) at 18/9 (93.5p) per ton & Wash stands @ 7/6 (37.5p) each, no roofing slate prices were quoted.

The Llwyngwern Slate Quarry Company Ltd was formed in 1863 to work here and at Glandulas, but they liquidated in 1866. H.J. Standly bought the effects and took over the lease, but his operation must have been modest as his 4-weekly wages bills in 1867 of around £45 would have only covered a dozen or so men inferring an annual output of at most 300 tons.

By 1878 T. Lloyd Jones trading as the Llwyngwern Slate & Slab Quarry was in possession, in that year he was pursuing a debt from Ellis and Owen, Slate Enamelling and Slate Manufacturers of Moor Street (now Cambrian Place), Aberystwyth, the quality of product being disputed. The debt was not, as one would expect, for Slab, but for roofing slates, 2600 of 14 x 10 Seconds sold @ 77/6 (£3.37) per mille, plus 4/ (20p) loading.

By 1883 35 men were employed, producing 915 tons. An abstract of figures for 1886-1888 suggest that monthly tonnages averaged 60-70. With a peak summer month, such as August '88 totalling 105 and a poor winter month, e.g. November '87 being under 31. With roofing slate 5-10% of make (by weight).

In 1888 David Llewellyn Jones and Thomas Ellis Morgan took a new lease from the Vanes Estate, but this was assigned two years later to Arthur Thomas Carr and William John Lewis, of the Towyn Enamelled Slate Quarry Company, although the quarry still traded as the Llwyngwern Quarry Co.

In 1891, there was an agreement with Will Roberts and John Jones to take over the company's enamelling works at Towyn, paying for stock-in-trade and agreeing to take slate from the quarry and to carry out enamelling and finishing work. Again that year there was trouble from a dis-satisfied customer, a Mr London, an Enamelled Slate manufacturer, being awarded £76.16 (£76.80) against them.

In 1893, reflecting the withdrawal from enamelling, the company was renamed, the Towyn Company, and two years later the lease was assigned to the new name, although that year the quarry was recorded as idle. Up and running again in 1894, they were again chasing debt, this time with Roberts & Co of Barry, not that they were all that prompt at settlement themselves as an overdue bill for the supply of coal to them by Stodharts of Cardiff was still being paid off in instalments.

Jeremiah Williams (late of Rhiw'r Gwreiddyn?) became manager and upped manpower to 70. In 1896 the Landlord's permission was obtained for a new tramway route, this may have been in connection with the long tunnel, which was cut at about this time. In 1897 Bennett Jones replaced Williams and by 1900 had 144 men, but money was clearly tight as they had mortgaged the quarry to P.C. Ash & A.L. Crockford in 1899 and a further mortgage was taken out a year later in their now changed name of Maglona Quarries Ltd.

In 1902 their output was 2087 tons, almost entirely Slab and mantelpieces, with employment down to under 100. Business continued to fall and at the end of 1904 they only had 42 men. In 1905 Maglona failed, with even preferential creditors only getting 2/6 (12½p) in the £1.

The next year Lewis joined with Peter Bennion, took over the lease, which they mortgaged to Evan Thomas for £5,000, who promptly re-mortgaged it on to Ash & Crockford. They obtained the landlord's approval to erect a ropeway to tip on the side of Glandulas Mawr and, puzzlingly, to erect "buildings" at that site.

By 1907 they had built the workforce up to 45 but were in arrears with the half yearly instalments of the £150 pa rent. In 1909, with now only 33 men at work, they negotiated a sale of the lease to Sidney Fowler Wright. The Vanes Estate however, made it clear that assignment could only be allowed if and when the arrears of rent were paid. By Easter 1910 the landlords tiring of repeated promises of "imminent" payment, direct the Bailiff to act, and in May a distress action was held.

The Particulars included —
2 Steam Engines & Boilers, powering the "Sawing Machines" and the "Overhead Tramway".
A Steam Crane and a "Drawing Machine" with Wire Rope.
40 Slab Sawing Tables and 11 Planing Machines.
3 Weighing Machines, 3 Turntables, Tramrails, 4 Block Cranes with Chains, a Crab Winch, Belting and 63 Pulleys, 3 Slate and

Zinc Cistern, a "Float", Vices, Anvil, Bellows, Earthenware Pipes, Shafting, Circular Saws, a Slate Drill, 19 Trams in the Quarry, 9 Iron trams "on the Railway", 3 Slab Cars and 24 "Rough" Slab Cars, a Dynamo, Office Furniture, 3 Ladders, a Chaffcutter, Stock of Slates and Slab and, (apparently the star item) a Strong Draught Horse and Gear. The 40' x 3' Waterwheel was listed but did not sell.

An interesting sequel to the sale is a payment to Elizabeth Woods of 3/4 (16p) per day, and re-imbursement for oats etc, for the 9 days prior to the sale that her husband, James, spent looking after the horse! And, of course there was Bailiff Roberts' fee of £2.15.0 (£2.75) for "minding" the plant before the sale. Several items originally listed, such as the Saw Sharpening Machine, the inevitable "Crate of Glass" (which every quarry had to replace the vulnerable mill roof-lights) and a donkey, were absent from the sale, so one is perhaps entitled to question the effectiveness of Roberts' vigilance.

However there were also acrimonious, but in retrospect, amusing sequels; Sidney Wright, although he had no title, had in fact been working the quarry, and he claimed that certain items sold were his, such as the coal, oil, grease & gunpowder. He emphasised that the track which he had laid in the "Lower Tunnel" was his, as well as the roll of unused belting "in the office", and some chimneypieces he claimed to have made.

Then Arthur Crockford showed up wanting to know where all the plant had gone on which his loan to Thomas was secured. He also claimed that he and Ash still had mortgage rights over the lease. He stated that a total of £13,000 was due to them and they intended to find a buyer for the quarry forthwith. Then a Mr Brooks appeared, flatly asserting that all the plant sold in the sale had previously been sold to him!

Evan Thomas, still owed £5,000 by Crockford and Ash, sportingly offered to take over the quarry in settlement, he even proposed a new 30 year lease, with, optimistically, an option to extend for a further 30 years!

An Edwin Davies expressed strong interest in buying the lease but from whom is not clear.

Meanwhile, Wright was seeking to continue working the quarry, maintaining that he had already paid Lewis and Bennion

£5,000 for it. He claimed that this figure included all the plant which had been disposed of at the sale. However as a reasonable man he suggested that matters might be squared by Lord Vane-Tempest "lending" him the now idle machinery at Braich Goch. This suggestion was not well received.

All the time the Estate was still seeking rent, which was accruing again since the sale, and was adamant that on-one could sell, assign or dispose of anything to anybody until arrears due to them were first cleared up. Bennion, who had made a 10/ (50p) in the £1 composition with other creditors, could not be found, Wright was declared bankrupt. The Estate then directed its attentions to Lewis who was upset at having all guns trained on him. Right up to late 1913 these arrears were still being sought.

In April 1920 the Slates Trade Gazette reported that a "new company" was to take over, this apparently being Hall Harber & Thorne Ltd described as suppliers of Slates, Cisterns, Electric Switchboards, Billiards Table Beds and plain & enamelled Chimney Pieces. H. Griffiths was manager with 18 men, increasing to 32 by 1925. In 1926 J.F.H. Arkley made enquiries with a view to buying, but no sale was made. By 1928 now trading as Llwyngwern Slate Quarry Ltd, with E. Lloyd as manager, they had 9 out of their 15 men shown as being underground. In 1934, under the new owners, the Grantham Slate Works Ltd, they were again classed as an open quarry with 30 men at work.

They sold up in 1937, the Sale Particulars listed the buildings with some precision —
Slate Mill 140' x 27', Sanding Plate Shop (?) 35'6" x 23', Smithy 29' x 18', Engine Room 18'6" x 27', Workshop 21' x 17', Gas Producer House 12'6" x 17'3", Garage 36'6" x 35'6", Office (2 floors) 27' x 15', Messroom 20' x 15', Quarry Engine House 31' x 18'.

The Plant List detailed virtually every piece of wire and switch, the main items being —
A Horizontal Electric Geared Winch with 120' Wire Rope and 3 hp 220v Motor in a Corrugated & Deal Shelter. A Vertical Electric Geared Winch with 50' of rope and 3 hp Motor, made by Butler Bros (Glasgow). A 3 ton "Derricking" Crane, with 100' of rope and 3hp Motor, a total of 739 yards of 2'3" rails, 2 Turntables & a 5 Ton Weighbridge. 9 Flat Trucks and 1 Wrought Iron Truck. ¾

mile 1½″ piping (from Reservoir to Mill). A Mather & Platt 220v 7.5hp Generator, 29 amp @ 730 rpm & 400′ Cable. A 18-20 hp "National" Horizontal Semi-Diesel with Air Compressor and Receiver. A 2¼hp Villiers 2-stroke engine. A Broome and Wade Single Cylinder Vertical Compressor (6′ x 8″) & 2 receivers & 266 yards of piping. 2 Pneumatic Drills.

The Mill was described as containing — an 8′ x 2″ Belt Driven "Sanding Plate" and another 6′6″ x 2.″, Gear Driven. What they described as a "Re-cutting Bench" by Turner Bros with a 6′6″ x 3′6″ Slotted "Facing Plate" (Table?) and another of 8′6″ x 5″ and a third 7′ x 3′6″, one by Webb & Co 7′ x 4′, 4 others of unspecified make, 6′6″ x 3′6″ and 4′ x 2′9″, 4′6″ x 3′6″ & 3′ x 3′, respectively. They listed 8 "Rough Cutting Benches", one 9′ x 5′ by Glaslyn Foundry and 7 of unspecified makes, 4 having 10′ x 7′ "Plates", one 10′6″ x 6′ and 2, 9′6″ x 7′, also a "Sundry Cutting Bench" 2′3″ x 3′. (17 saws in all). There were 2, Rack & Pinion Planing machines, one 8′ x 3′6″, the other 8′6″ x 3′6″. 1 Saw Sharpening Machine, also a "Dismantled" Planing Machine.

The Engine House contained a Crossley HD10 Horizontal heavy-oil Engine, 40-44 hp, single cylinder with flywheel, air receiver and Ballata belting, also a 40 hp single cylinder Gas Engine. There was a "National" Gas Producer Plant described as "Complete". A Dodge lorry was included. It is of note that even at this date the Office Equipment included a letter press. Oddly there were no Chains, Blocks, Ladders etc such as one would normally expect to find.

F.M. Round and D. Round then took it on, trading as the Llwyngwern Slate Quarries Ltd with 15 men. The next year, 1938, reclassified as a mine, they had 10 men, 2 being underground.

In 1945 the Inspector of Mines reported "discontinued 1941" although, oddly he showed J. Hughes as manager. This report was repeated in 1950 with G.S. Ellison shown as manager. Some working was done until the early 1950s, there being a scheme in 1953 to make bricks from the quarry waste. Such machinery as remained was scrapped in 1959.

Description

The original hillside quarry was connected to the (originally) water powered mill by an incline. When extraction progressed downward, a tramway ran out on the level, via a tunnel. Steam was introduced in the 1900s, with diesel later. An incline from the mill led to the Corris Railway branch.

As overburden and the position of the lower reservoir limited the advance of the working face, the working was deepened into a pit, with some underground chambering. It is clear that some extensive pit working and chambering was envisaged as a tunnel was bored from the foot of the exit incline, under the mill area to a point below the quarry, as was done at Abercwmeiddaw, (shown on the 1901 O.S.). It did serve as a drain, and in 1909 Wright laid rails, although it is unlikely that it was ever actually employed as an exit route.

Owing to limited tipping space a wire rope conveyor, steam powered, took rubbish up to a dump, high on the hillside, but this arrangement, put in during 1900s does not seem to have been a success.

The plan accompanying the 1937 Sale Particulars shows a tramway in the quarry running, via a tunnel, past a rake of buildings, to the mill and also looping round the mill. This loop rejoins the line from the mill to the head of incline where a branch runs to the tip. At the foot of incline, apart from the line going directly to the C.R. bridge, a branch turns south in the present car-park area. There is a small building (office?) shown where the foot of the present passenger lift now is. The tip and building on the hillside are not shown.

Remains

The mills area is now occupied by the National Centre for Alternative Technology who have made good use of some of the buildings. There is rail on the ground and some quarry artifacts are still around. The main quarry is reached by the short access tunnel. Within are some loading platforms, the remains of a derrick and the base for a haulage winch. There is some chambering on either side.

Above the access tunnel is the presumed lower mounting for the ropeway. At a higher level are rubbish runs from early working, and above again, the upper site with a building, the top mounting of the ropeway and some tipping. The reservoirs are still in use as a water source. The drainage tunnel emerges at the foot of the recent (1991) water balanced incline which takes visitors up to the mills level. The abutments of the railway bridge across the Dulas can be seen and the high embanked approach causeway to it is a notable feature.

PANDY SH760081 (Also known as Cloddfa Fronfelin) (34)
This was an optimistic attempt to find the Vein being worked at Cwm Era, by tunnelling south. Abandoned at an early stage, but a second attempt was said to have been made by Pickstone after he bought the estate in 1908.
Description
At least one adit, possibly two, some start made to erect buildings.
Remains
Excavation & spoil. Wheelpit and some stonework of never completed surface structures.

PANTPERTHOG SH748054 (17)
Trial only.
Description
Underground, single adit only.
Remains
Run-in adit alongside forestry road.

RHIW'R GWREIDDYN SH760054 ("Jeremiah") (32)
Believed to have been opened around 1818, it was run for many years, by Hugh Pugh.

The property which included 2 cottages, a smithy and a chapel, was bought from William Pugh in 1846 by Fredrick L. Cooper & H.J. Barton, Hugh Davies of Machynlleth and G.W. Bonsall also having an interest. The quarry being then occupied by Thomas Edwards.

In 1854 the Rev. P.A. Cooper (son of F.L.?), let the quarry to David Edwards, this does not seem to have lasted long as there were further letting negotiations in 1863, offering it at a rent of £25 for the first year, £50 for each of the next 3 years and £150 per year thereafter, merging to a royalty of 2/ (10p) per ton on "best" slate and 1/6 (7.5p) on slab and "2nd class' products. There were no takers, although John Lloyd Jones of the Britannia Slate & Slab Co of Nantlle did show serious interest. Even with slate prices rising, and railed transport a possibility, the Rev. Cooper could not get a steady let, and little regular work seems to have been done.

It was eventually taken by Jeremiah Williams in 1878. Williams did a lot of work for scant return, as prices were dropping back and he was handicapped by the lack of direct rail access. A Mining Journal report of 1880 described it as, "not being worked as much as it has been", adding sourly that "its decline is not due to the poorness of the rock".

In 1884 he was employing 12 men but was in serious trouble and distraint was made on his plant. The sale Particulars which were described as "The whole of the quarry materials" made a pathetic showing — "Overshot Water Wheel 40′ x 3′. 1000 yards of Tramrail, 1 Drum 8′6″ x 4′6″, 660 feet of wire rope, 10 carriages and rollers, a turntable, 115′ of 3′ water trough 2 iron trams, 'some' slab trucks and frames". There was no mention of saws or any mill equipment.

The following year Evan Reese came to the "rescue" offering to buy the quarry for £5,500 and suggesting a £275 deposit, which possibly was never actually paid. He was, of course, putting together his grand scheme which would have merged this quarry with the Esgairgeiliog Works and the Era quarry. At one point he tried to hive off this quarry, from the intended combine, by letting it on a year's lease at £40 plus 2/ (10p) per ton Royalty.

When Reese went bankrupt in 1889, W.J. Lewis of the Towyn Enamelling Co, (later the Towyn Co, later Maglona) picked up the pieces, but at that time, he was not in good financial shape for, in 1892 there was, after some negotiation over prices, an urgent order placed with Stothart of Cardiff for a truck of best semi-bitumenous coal @18/9 (93p) per ton to be sent to Machynlleth station. Not only did Stothart not get paid but they failed to get their truck back! 18 months later, the company finally agreed to pay up the £30 due, including costs and truck demurrage, at the rate of 10/ (50p) per week! A.J. Williams was manager possibly a relative of Jeremiah Williams, the late owner.

In 1899, 69 men were employed, and several years of comparative prosperity followed, when the northern section was developed. The lease was renewed for 42 years in 1901, but by then, under David Hughes' management manning was down to 24, Maglona got into difficulties in 1905 and shortly afterwards, O.

Jones and E.J.S. Bryant (London slate merchants) took over, trading as New Rhiw'r Gwreiddyn employing about 10 men.

They seem to have done little work but things started to move when D.E. Jones of New Era took possession just prior to WW1, but he suspended work in 1916. W. Horton re-opened it in 1920 with H. Griffiths as manager and 11 men, but by 1928 employment was down to 5 men. Subsequently it was run on a small scale, until 1934 as an outpost of Braich Goch.

Description

The earlier, southern workings were open, developing into a pit. Material was originally brought down to a water powered mill by incline, but as the workings deepened it was hauled out on the level.

The northern quarry (not on the 1891 O.S.), had a tramway going to a tipping area near the river, bridging the then public road, which at that time, was nearer the river than the present road, and at a lower level. The older quarry also had a tramway leading to this same bridge, which additionally served to bring block from the northern site to the mill. The present road defines the line of that tramway and also the approximate line of a launder which brought water from Ceinws.

In spite of the relative proximity of the Corris Railway no connection was ever made. The site was later used for the making of hospital furniture.

Remains

On the southern site there is much tipping from early work and a flooded pit. There is a weigh-house and a redundant drumhouse converted into a lean-to shelter, (possibly a power house). A fine range of buildings remain, some in re-use, consisting of a double mill and a rake of ancillary structures, later altered and extended in brick. There is a small reservoir, with piping to a turbine housing (which may have replaced a water wheel). A covered channel carries the tailrace under the stocking area. There is the remnant of a furnace in one building, but whether this is a quarrying relic or from the later re-use is not known. On the northern site there is little but the excavations themselves.

The abutments of the tramway bridge to the tipping area near the river still stand. The surface of the old road, which passed beneath it, is discernable.

TARRAN CADIAN SH733070 (7)

Little more than a trial, but some make may have come out. Bowen Jones writing in 1905 refers to recent trials made in Cwm Cadian by Evan Reese, and that he had worked it for about 6 years. Reese employed 3 men there in 1903.

Description

Apparently just a single adit, presumably with some chambering.

Remains

A 10 yard adit leads to a fall, now inaccessible in thick forestry.

Section 9 ENAMELLING

Traditionally it was by no means unknown for some slate products to have a decorative finish applied, originally just paint but later stove enamel. By the middle of the 19th C., a small but significant, industry had developed. One could be derogatory about the disguising of a fine natural material such as slate, but at a time, particularly in the vicinity of the quarries, when slate was a commonplace material, one can understand the wish to give it a more exotic appearance. No different, perhaps from the practice of making cast iron and, at a later date, plastics, resemble less mundane materials.

Mainly applied to fireplaces, but also to a wide variety of domestic items and to many of the household ornaments indispensable to Victorian homes. The finish could be solid colour or contrived to give the appearance of marble or wood. Indeed a fireplace, in black, with incised grooves picked out in gold and possibly with painted panels, must have been a thing of great beauty.

Latterly enamelling was widely used in the production of electrical switchboard panels. A gloss black finish usually being specified.

Old recipes called for Tar Varnish, lead pigments mixed with Copal Varnish, Benzolene, Turps and so on, with complex instructions for their application and astonishingly some mentioned "slate grey" finishes! Application was either by brushing or dipping, or in more recent times, by spraying.

It was a skilled and lengthy process. First the slate had to be dried at a moderate heat of 70-80°F for days or even weeks, then prior to enamelling, pre-heated, and afterwards stoved at 220°F with a gradual cooling to around 120°F. Failure to dry properly or to cool slowly, particularly with thicker slabs, would result in cracking. Consistent success called for considerable experience.

The Corris area was unusual in that a substantial proportion of their Slab was used for enamelled products. This may have been because Corris Slab was more resistant to thermal shock than that from other districts. Correspondence exists from enamellers to other quarries, alleging cracking etc, but no documents of complaint have been found relating to Corris quarries.

As with some other "downstream" processes enamelling was normally carried out by firms independent of and remote from the quarries, where perhaps the price of coal was less. For example Inigo Jones at Groeslon, (where one oven is still in existence) also, Sessions at Gloucester and Cardiff, Newport Enamelled Slate Co, Aberystwyth Enamelling and Marble Co, as well as E. Matthews of London, were regular buyers of Corris Slab.

Some enamellers, to secure supplies "back integrated", taking control of quarries for themselves. The Towyn Co. getting involved with Llwyngwern and other quarries, being an example of this. Most notable is Inigo Jones, sited almost within sight of quarries at Nantlle, buying Cymerau quarry to ensure Slab supplies of Corris quality. This was to be later repeated when the Lloyd brothers of the Bow Slate and Enamel company, successors to E. Matthews, bought Aberllefenni.

Rarely did quarries have enamelling departments themselves, but this did occur at Braich Goch and Escairgeiliog. Also Ratgoed seems to have had some involvement as, just possibly, did Rhiw'r Gwreiddyn.

Unique to Corris however, was the setting up of a plant in a quarrying area by an independent processor. This was —

MATTHEWS MILL SH768091 (43)

When John Davies of Aberllefenni died in 1827 a "Water Corn & Grist Mill at Aberllefenni" was referred to as lately being in the possession of Robert Jones, who had been working Aberllefenni quarry. These may have been the original premises which T.E. Magnus first occupied, before "Y Magnus" or Matthew's Mill was used. Magnus, who owned quarries at Valentia, Ireland and an "ornamental slate works" in Pimlico, was by the mid 19thC., well known for his enamelling process (patented in 1830), as well as for Writing Slate manufacture.

An advertisement in the "Illustrated London News' of 1st August, 1857 for "Magnus Enamelled Slate" instances uses for its products as "Chimney pieces, Cabinet formed stoves, Stove fronts, Bath & washstand tops, Pedestals, Slabs for console and ornamental table tops, Marbled wall linings, pilasters etc for halls & vestibules, plain ditto for dairies, larders, baths and wash-houses, urinals etc. Vases, fonts, altars, mural tablets, monuments, tombs etc." They go on to boast of their medals from the Society of Arts and from the Great Exhibition of 1851 and of their 2 (first class!) medals at the Paris Exhibition. They conclude with the claim that their product was "Handsomer, stronger, more durable and cheaper by far, than marble".

An offer for sale of the Aberllefenni Estate in 1859 refers to "All the apparatus for carrying on Magnus' beautiful process of enamelling". There was also reference to it in 1862 as "Enamelling works".

Magnus having gone out of business in 1872, Ashton and Green took a 7 year lease in 1889 at £10 pa, but almost immediately got leave from the Pryces of Aberllefenni to assign it to Ernest Matthews who traded, initially as Ashton, Green & Roberts. Matthews took a fresh lease from A.R. Pryce in October 1895 of a "Mill and Premises at Aberllefenni Slate Quarries" with rights to water and a water channel, rights for a tramway from the Corris Railway to the mill and authority to construct a waterwheel which would remain the lessee's property. It was for 14 years from March 1896 at a rental of £13 pa. It was clearly set out that Matthews must only work Aberllefenni slabs, insofar as they were able to supply his needs.

This document would seem to have authorised re-alignment of the previous branch from the Corris Railway, (which had obviated having to slide blocks across the road on timber planks). Also the re-installation of a waterwheel, presumably after a period of idleness. This lease was re-negotiated in 1904 for 21 years at £15 pa but the house Tremafon, oddly, for 20 years only.

Ernest Matthews & Co. of Matthews Mill were listed in a Machynlleth trades directory of 1910. H.H. Disley "Slate Works" was also separately listed, this is odd as H.H. Disley was a partner with Ernest Matthews by this time. Disley was also the local rates collector, it being then the custom in villages, to have a part time collector. In 1919, he was in dispute with Gilliart, Lord Vane-Tempest's agent over the rating of the disused engine-shed at Braich Goch quarry. In 1921 the Matthews lease was surrendered, Pryce granting a new lease to J. & W. Henderson of Aberdeen for 21 years at £45 pa of what were described as "Enamelling Premises".. In 1929 this lease was assigned to Slate Slab Products Ltd of London EC3, who purchased the remainder of the lease, the house "Tremafon", the mill, enamelling building and premises at Aberllefenni Slate quarries for £1534.10.0 (£1534.50).

This company intended to "develop the business of Ernest Matthews at Bow, Aberllefenni and Corris, and of Sessions & Sons at Gloucester and Cardiff". They were to have "sole selling rights, world-wide (except Portugal and its colonies) of the output of Velango Slate and Marble quarries and from Major A.H. Pryce, the output of Aberllefenny". Exports were to be handled by The Slate Products Export Company.

Operations here seem to have ceased in 1931 when Pryce took possession, enamelling thereafter being confined to Braich Goch.

The Ernest Matthews story has an interesting sequel —
In 1921 Mr Lloyd, a quarryman, himself a quarryman's son, despairing of finding steady employment in Corris, moved to London, where he obtained work with Ernest Matthews & Co at their slate finishing works there. His son Dewi followed him into the firm, becoming a foreman at 18.

In 1937 father and son bought out the company, renaming it the Bow Slate and Enamel Co Ltd. Mr Lloyd senior having died in 1943, Dewi's brother Gwilym joined him in the business. Almost paradoxically they suffered from post war problems as had their father a generation before. The effect on the father had been shortage of work, on the sons, shortage of slate. This eventually caused them to buy the Aberllefenni quarry and, later, the same Braich Goch quarry where once their forebears had worked. The business afterwards being carried on by Dewi's son John F. Lloyd.

Description

A building of conventional slate mill pattern, with a water-wheel at one end housing saws etc. Between it and the river was the smaller enamelling building. Alongside, close to the road was a weigh-house.

Remains

Bryn Derw house is a comparatively modern structure on the site of the weigh-house. Both the mill and the enamelling building have entirely vanished, having been demolished in 1953. There are vestiges of the tip at the rear of Bryn Derw. Tremafon still stands as do cottages, possibly associated with the mill, on the far side of the river.

The route of the tramway branch is clearly defined by the usual slate fence. Alongside the road is a stone pillar that was a support for a removable slide for handling block across the road, prior to the rail connection. The leat is traceable.

CORRIS MILL SH755079 (not referenced)
Whilst no enamelling connection has been established, it is believed that some slate process was carried out here. The 1859 Aberllefenni Estate sale included "Pandy-Corris", let to Hughes Humphrey (Humphrey Hughes?). it was subsequently enlarged and apparently adapted for slate purposes.
Description
A fulling mill building adapted.
Remains
Parts of the original walls on the east bank of the river, in the lane opposite Corris Post Office have been incorporated into a modern shed.

PANTPERTHOG MILL SH749042 (not referenced)
There is anecdotal reference to at least, an intention, to process slate in or near the fulling mill here. A lease of 1895 to Thomas Pugh, refers to a "factory".

SOURCES

Selected Bibliography

Anon; *A Return to Corris*, (Corris Rly Soc., 1988)

Boyd, J.I.C.; *Narrow Gauge Railways in Mid Wales* (Oakwood, 1970)

Baughan, P.E.; *A Regional History of the Railways of G.B. Vol 11* (David & Charles, 1980)

Cozens, L.; *The Corris Railway* (Corris Rly Soc, (rep), 1992)

Davies, D.C.; *Slate & Slate Quarrying* (Crosby, Lockwood, 1878)

Dodd, A.H.; *The Industrial Revolution in North Wales* (U of W Press, 1971)

Isherwood, G.; *Slate* (A.B. Publishing, 1988)

Jones, E.; *Bargen Dinorwig* (Tŷ ar y Graig, 1980)

Jones, R.M.; *The North Wales Quarrymen 1874-1922* (Cardiff U of W, 1982)

Kellow, J.; *The Slate Trade of N. Wales* (Mining Journal, 1868)

Lewis, M.J.T. (Ed); *The Slate Quarries of North Wales in 1873* (S.N.P. Study Centre, 1987)

Lindsay, J.; *The History of the North Wales Slate Industry* (David & Charles, 1974)

Morgan, Scott; *Corris, a Narrow Gauge Portrait* (Irwell Press, 1991)

North, R.J.; *Slates of Wales* (Nat. Mus. of Wales, 1925)

Owen, R.; *Diwydiannau Col*

Parry, B.R. (Ed); *Chwareli a Chwarelwyr* (Gwynedd A.S., 1974)

Rees, D.M.; *The Industrial Archaeology of Wales* (David & Charles, 1975)

Richards, A.J.; *A Gazeteer of the Welsh Slate Industry* (Gwasg Carreg Gwalch, 1991)

Richards, A.; *Slate Quarrying and how to make it Profitable* Watts & Co

Tomos, D.; *Llechi Lleu* (Argraffdy Arfon, 1980)

Williams, J.A.; *Trem yn Ôl* (1962)

Williams, M.; *The Slate Industry* (Shire Publications, 1991)

Reports

Report of the Departmental Committee upon Merionethshire Slate Mines (1895)

Inspector of Mines Reports (1875 on)

Journals

The Mining Journal (1846-1891)

The Quarry Manager's Journal (Vols 14 on)

The Slate Trades Gazette (1912-1926)

Theses

Pritchard, D.; *The Slate Industry of North Wales 1780-1935*) (UCNW, 1935)

Ellis, G.; *A History of the Slate Quarryman in Caernarfonshire in the 19th C.* (UCNW, 1931)

Archive Material

The Machynlleth Papers & other deposited records (National Library of Wales)
J.S. Wilkinson & other deposits (Caernarfon R.O.)
Various deposits (Dolgellau R.O.)
Home Office lists of Mines, various dates
Aberllefenni Slate Quarry records. Wincilate Ltd (Private collection)

INDEX OF QUARRIES